D0970837

The finest Legends of the Rhine

The Lorelei

The finest Legends of the Rhine

by

Wilhelm Ruland

Small edition

With 10 Illustrations

Verlag von Hoursch & Bechstedt in Köln

The publishers desire to thank
Mr. Andrew Mitchell and
Mr. H. J. Findlay, Edin-
burgh, for valuable assistance
in the preparation of the new
English edition.

Printed by Ernst Knoth, Melle (Germany) 1936

Contents

5

Worms

The Nibelungen Song

*

To-day we are deeply touched, as our forefathers must have been, at the recital of the boundless suffering and the overwhelming concatenation of sin and expiation in the lives of the Recken and Frauen of the Nibelungen Legend. That naive singer has remained nameless and unknown, who about the end of the 12th century wrote down this legend in poetic form, thus preserving forever our most precious relic of Germanic Folksepic. A powerful story it is of sin and suffering: corresponding to the world itself and just as the primitive mind of a people loves to represent it. The story begins as a lovely idyll but ends in gloomy tragedy.

The ancient Rhenish town of Worms was during the great migrations the seat of authority of the Burgundian invaders, an east Germanic stock. During the glorious reign of King Gunther there appears, attracted by the beauty of Chriemhild the king's sister, a young hero, Siegfried, by name. He is himself a king's son, his father Siegmund reigning in Xanten „nieden by dem Rine". King Gunther receives the fair Recken into his service as a vassal.

Siegfried, exhibiting the fairest loyalty to his overlord, and rendered invisible by magic, conquers for him the redoubtable Brunhild, the proud queen of the island kingdom of Isenland (Iceland) and compels her to wed King Gunther. As a reward Siegfried receives the hand of Chriemhild. In the fulness of his heart the hero presents to Chriemhild as a marriage gift, the Nibelungen Hoard, which he had gained in his early years from the sons of the king of the Nibelungen and from Dwarf Alberich the guardian of the treasure.

Joy reigns in the king's court at Worms, but it was not shared by all. Besides Chriemhild there was another secretly drawn towards the hero, and in Brunhild's heart the bridal happiness of Chriemhild awakens such envy that soon no friendly word passes between the women. They become estranged and one day her bad feeling leads Brunhild to harsh words. Then alas, Chriemhild gave unbridled licence to her tongue. In her rash insolence she represents to Brunhild that it was not Gunther but Siegfried who formerly overcame her. As proof of this she produces the ring and girdle which Siegfried had taken on that night from the powerful Brunhild, and which he had presented to Chriemhild. With fierce haughtiness Chriemhild taunts her opponent with a hateful name no woman could endure, and forbids her to enter the cathedral.

Brunhild, weeping, informs King Gunther of the contumely heaped upon her. The king is filled with wrath, and his vassal, the gloomy Hagen considers how he may destroy Siegfried avowedly to avenge the Queen, but secretly for the possession of the Nibelungen Hoard. During a hunt in the Odenwald Siegfried was treacherously stabbed by Hagen whilst stooping to drink from a well. The intention was to spread the report that Siegfried had been slain by robbers whilst hunting alone. So, on the following day they crossed the Rhine back to Worms.

In the night Hagen caused the dead body of Siegfried to be laid in front of Chriemhild's chamber. In the early morning as Chriemhild accompanied by her attendants was preparing to go to mass in the cathedral she noticed the corpse of her hero. A wail of sorrow arose. Chriemhild threw herself weeping on the body of her murdered husband. "Alas!" she cried "thy shield is not hewn by swords: thou hast been foully murdered. Did I but know who has done this, I would avenge thy death." Chriemhild ordered a magnificent bier for her royal hero, and demanded that an ordeal should be held over the corpse. "For it is a marvellous thing, and to this day it happens, that when the bloodstained murderer approaches wounds bleed anew."

So all the princes and nobles of Burgundy walked past the dead body, above which was the figure of the crucified Redeemer of the world, and lo! when the grim Hagen came forward the wounds of the dead man began to flow. In the presence of the astounded men and horrified women Chriemhild accused Hagen of the assassination of her husband.

Much treachery and woe accompanied the expiation of this great crime. The Nibelungen Hoard, the cause of the shameful deed, was sunk in the middle of the Rhine in order to prevent future strife arising from human greed. But Chriemhild's undying sorrow was not mitigated, nor her unconquerable thirst for revenge appeased.

After the burial of his son King Siegmund begged in vain that Chriemhild should come to the royal city of Xanten; she remained at Worms for thirteen years constantly near her beloved dead.

Then the sorrowing woman removed to the Abbey of Lorch which her mother, Frau Ute, had founded. Thither also, she transferred Siegfried's body.

When Etzel (Attila) the ruler of the Huns wooed her, Chriemhild urged not by love but by very different feelings gave him her hand and accompanied her heathen lord to the Ungarnland. Then she treacherously invited Siegfried's murderers to visit her husband, and prepared for them a destruction which fills the mind with horror. The Burgundian king and his followers, who, since the Hoard had come into their possession, were called the Nibelungen, fell slaughtered in the Etzelburg under the swords of the Huns and their allies, thus atoning for their faithlessness to the hero Siegfried. And with this awful holocaust ends the Song of the Nibelungen Not, the most renowned heroic legend in the German tongue.

Frankfort
The Knave of Bergen

*

The emperor was to be crowned at
Frankfort, and great festivities were to
be given in the town in his honour,
among them a masquerade, at which
knights and noble ladies rivalled each
other in splendour. Joy was depicted on
every face at this great assembly, only
one knight among the many guests being
noticeable for his gravity and restraint.
He wore black armour, and the feather
waving above his visor was black too. No
one knew him or could guess who he was.
He approached the empress with a noble
grace, bent his knee, and asked her to
dance with him, which she graciously consented to do. He glided gracefully through

13

the splendid halls with the queen of the festival, and soon every eye was turned on them, and everyone was eager to know who he was.

The empress was charmed with her excellent partner, and the grace of his refined conversation pleased her so much that she granted him a second and a third dance.

Everyone became more and more curious to know who this masked knight was. Meanwhile the hour struck when every mask had to be raised, and every masked guest must make himself known. More than all the others the empress was anxious to know who her partner was. But he hesitated and even refused to take off his mask until she ordered him peremptorily to do so. The knight obeyed, but none of the high ladies or noble knights recognised him. Suddenly two stewards pressed through the crowd, crying out with indignation and horror;

"It is the headsman from Bergen!"

Then the emperor in great wrath ordered the shameful offender who had thus degraded the empress and insulted his sovereign to be led to execution.

But the culprit, throwing himself at the emperor's feet, said boldly, "I have transgressed, my lord, and offended you and your noble guests, but most heavily have I sinned against my queen. No punishment, not even blood, will be able to wash out the disgrace you have suffered through me. Therefore, oh King! allow me to propose a remedy to efface the shame. Draw your sword and knight me, and I will throw down my gauntlet to any one who dares to speak disrespectfully of my sovereign".

The emperor was taken by surprise at this bold proposal. However it appeared the wisest plan to adopt.

"You are a knave," he replied after a moment's consideration, "but your advice is good and displays prudence, just as your offence shows adventurous courage. Well then," — laying his sword on the man's neck — "rise Sir Knight. You have acted like a knave, and the Knave of Bergen you shall be called henceforth."

A joyful shout of approbation pealed through the halls, and the new knight "Schelm von Bergen" again glided gracefully through the crowd with the queen of the festival.

Johannisberg

*

Wherever the German tongue is heard, and even further still, the king of all Rhine wines, "Johannisberger" is known and sought after. Every friend of the grape which grows on the banks of this river is well acquainted with it, but few perhaps know of its princely origin. It is princely, not because princes' hands once kept the key to Johannisberg, but rather because princely hands planted the vine in the Rhine country, and this royal giver was no other than Charlemagne, the all-powerful ruler of the kingdom of the Franks.

16

Once in early spring Charles the Great was standing on the balcony of his castle at Ingelheim, his eyes straying over the beautiful stretch of country at his feet. Snow had fallen during the night, and the hills of Rüdesheim were clothed in white. As the imperial ruler was looking thoughtfully over the landscape, he noticed that the snow on one side of Johannisberg melted quicker in the sun's rays than on any other part. Charles, who was a great and deep thinker, began to reflect that on a spot where the rays of the sun shone so genially, something better than grass would thrive.

Sending for Kunrat his faithful servant, he bade him saddle his horse the next day at dawn and ride to Orleans, a town famous for its good wine. He was to inform the citizens that the emperor had not forgotten the excellent wine they had given him there, and that he would like to grow the same vines on the Rhine. He desired the citizens of Orleans therefore to send him plants from their country.

The messenger set off to do the king's bidding and ere the moon had again gone round her course, was back in the castle at Ingelheim. Great satisfaction prevailed at court. Charles, mighty ruler as he was, even went so far as to cross to Rüdesheim, where he planted with his royal hand the French vine in German soil.

This was no mere passing whim on the part of the emperor. He sent messengers constantly to bring word how the vines were thriving in Rüdesheim and on the flanks of Johannisberg, and when the third autumn had come round, the Emperor Charlemagne set out from his favourite resort, Aix-la-Chapelle, for the Rhine country, and great rejoicing prevailed among the vine-reapers from Rüdesheim to Johannisberg.

The first cup of wine was solemnly offered to the emperor, a golden wine in a golden goblet, a wine worthy of a king.

Charles took a long deep draught, and with brightened eyes praised the delicious drink. It became his favourite wine, this fiery "Johannisberger", making him young again in his old age. What Charlemagne then felt when he drank this wine, every one who raises the sparkling grapejuice to his lips is keenly sensible of also. Wherever the German tongue is heard, and even further still, the king of all Rhine wines is known and sought after, Johannisberger wine.

The legend weaves another wonderful tale about the great emperor blessing his grapes.

A poet's pen has fashioned it into a song, which is still often heard among the grapegatherers.

Every spring when the vines are blossoming on the hills and in the valleys along the river, and their fragrance scents the air, a tall shadow wanders about the vineyards at night, a purple mantle hanging from his stately shoulders, and a crown on his head. It is Charlemagne, the great Emperor, who planted the grapes long years before. The luscious scent of the blossoms wakens him up from his tomb in Aix-la-Chapelle, and he comes to bless the grapes.

When the full moon gently casts her bright beams on the water, lighting up the emperor's nightly path, he may be seen crossing the golden bridge formed by her rays and then wandering further along the hills, blessing the vines on the other side of the river.

At the first crow of the cock he returns to his grave in Aix-la-Chapelle, and sleeps till the scent of the grapes wakens him next spring, when he again wanders through the countries along the Rhine, blessing the vineyards.

———

Let us now relate another little story which is told of the monks who lived at Johannisberg.

Once the high Abbot of Fulda came unexpectedly to visit the cloister at Johannisberg just about the time when the grapes were ripe. The worthy Abbot made

The Knave of Bergen

many inquiries about his people, showed himself highly pleased with the works of the industrious monks, and as a mark of his continued favour, invited all the inmates of the cloister to a drinking bout.

"Wine maketh the heart glad," thus quoting King David's significant words, the holy man began his speech: "God's loving hand will be gracious in future years to your vines. Let us profit by his grace, brothers, and drink what he has provided for us in moderation and reverence. But before we refresh ourselves with God's good gifts, take your breviaries and let us begin with a short prayer."

"Breviaries!" was whispered along the rows, and the eyes of the fat genial faces blinked in helpless embarassment.

"Yes, your breviaries," and the white-haired Abbot looked silently but sternly at the brothers.

They searched and searched.

Gradually the frown disappeared from the Abbot's face, and a smile gradually spread over his withered features.

"Well, never mind, let us drink," said he. Then feeling his pockets, he said with a gleam in his eye, "That's too bad! I ought to have brought a corkscrew with me when I came to the Rhine."

A corkscrew! Every one dives his hand into his pocket, and as many corkscrews were produced before the worthy Abbot as there were brothers present.

Then a gleam of merriment beamed in the Abbot's eyes.

"Bravo, ye pious monks! what a plentiful supply of corkscrews! Do not all look so embarrassed, we shall not be annoyed about it today but — to-morrow! Now we shall sing with King David. Wine maketh the heart glad," and the uncorked bottle went the rounds.

Ingelheim
Eginhard and Emma

I.

The story which we have now to relate is a very touching one, and it becomes even more interesting when we know that it is based on real fact.

In the little town of Ingelheim there was a beautiful marble castle, the favourite residence of Charlemagne. He often retired to this lonely, peaceful spot accompanied only by a few of his faithful vassals and the members of his own family. Eginhard, the emperor's private secretary, was never missing from this little circle. Charlemagne thought highly of this man, then in the prime of youth, on account of his profound knowledge and extraordinary talents.

The young scholar, so different from the wise councillors not only in his learning but in his cultivated manners, was a great favourite among the ladies of the court.

Eginhard who was a constant companion of the emperor, had also become an intimate member of the family circle, and Charlemagne entrusted him with the education of his favourite child Emma, daughter of his wife Gismonda. This dark-eyed maiden was considered the most beautiful of her age, and the young scholar could not long remain cold and indifferent to her charms. The undisturbed hours which should have been spent in learning, led to a mutual understanding. Eginhard struggled to remind himself of his duty towards his sovereign, but love overcame him, and soon an oath of eternal fidelity united these young hearts.

II.

The great emperor ought to have known what would be the consequence of allow-ing the young scholar to enjoy the society of his dark-eyed, passionate daughter. In the still hours of the night when all the inmates of the castle lay wrapped in sleep, Eginhard sought the chamber of his beloved. She listened enchanted to the glowing words of his burning heart, but their love was chaste and pure, no gusts of passion troubling them.

But fate was against these lovers. One night they were sitting in Emma's chamber talking confidentially together. The great palace was veiled in darkness, no ray of light, no star was to be seen in the heavens. As Eginhard was about to leave the chamber, he perceived that the courtyard below was covered with snow. It would have been impossible to pass across it without leaving a trace behind him, but at all risks he must reach his room.

What was to be done? Love is ingenious. After considering for some time together, they both concluded that there was but one way to prevent their being betrayed. The slender maiden took her lover on her back and carried him across the courtyard, thus leaving behind only her small footprints.

It happened that Charles the Great had not yet sought the repose he needed so much, as care banished sleep from his eyes. He sat at his window and looked out into the silent night. In the courtyard below he perceived a shadow crossing the pavement and, looking carefully, he recognised his favourite daughter Emma carrying a man on her back. — Yes! and this man was Eginhard his great favourite. Pain and anger struggled in his heart. He wanted to rush down and kill him — an emperor's daughter and a mere secretary — but with a great effort he restrained himself, mastered the violent agitation which this unexpected sight caused him, and went back to his chamber to wait wearily for dawn.

III.

The next day Charles assembled his councillors. They were all horrified to see his ghastly look; his brow was dark, and sorrow was depicted on every feature. Eginhard looked at his master apprehending coming evil. Charlemagne stood up and spoke: —

"What does a royal princess deserve, who receives the visit of a man at night?" The councillors looked at each other speechless. Eginhard's countenance became white as death. The councillors soon guessed the name of the royal princess, and they consulted together for some time not knowing what to say, but at last one councillor answered: —

"Your Majesty, we think that a weak woman must not be punished for anything done out of love."

"And what does a favourite of the emperor deserve who creeps into a royal princess' chamber at night?"

Charlemagne cast a dark look at his secretary, who trembled and became even paler. "Alas! all is lost," murmured he to himself. Then, raising his voice, he said, "Death, my Master and Emperor!"

Charles looked at the young man full

of astonishment. The wrath in his soul melted at this self-accusation and fervent repentance. Deep silence followed this answer, and in a few minutes the emperor dismissed his councillors, making a sign at the same time to Eginhard to follow him.

Without a word Charles led him into his private chamber, where in answer to his summons, Emma appeared.

Her heart misgave her as she saw the dark look on her father's face and the troubled features of her beloved. She understood all at once, and with a convulsive cry of pain threw herself at her father's feet.

„Mercy! mercy! my father, we love each other so dearly!" murmured she, raising her large eyes imploringly. "Mercy!" murmured Eginhard too, bending his knees.

The emperor remained silent. After a time he began to speak earnestly and coldly at first, but his voice changed to a milder tone on hearing the sobs of his favourite child.

"I shall not separate you who are bound to each other by love. A priest shall unite you, and at dawn to-morrow you must both be gone from the castle, never to return."

He left them, shutting the door behind him.

The beautiful maiden sank down on her knees, only half conscious in her grief of what her father had said. But Eginhard's soft voice soon whispered in her ear.

"Do not weep, Emma. By thrusting you from him, your father, my master, has only bound us together for ever. Come," he continued in a trembling voice, alarmed at her passionate tears, "we must go, but love will be ever with us."

The next day two pilgrims left the castle of Ingelheim, and took the road in the direction of Mayence.

IV.

Time wore on.

Charles the Great had made war on Saxony, had set the Roman crown upon his own head, and had become famous throughout the whole world. But all his fame had not prevented his hair from becoming grey, nor his heart from being sad. A mournful picture had imprinted itself on his mind, despite all his efforts to forget the past. In the evening when the setting sun glittered on the marble pillars of the royal palace, casting its golden rays into the chamber of the great emperor, it would find him sitting motionless in his carved oak-chair, his grey head buried in his hands, mournful dreams troubling his peace. He was thinking of the days which were past, of the young man whose gentle ways made him so different from the rough warriors of the court, how he used to recite poetry and sing the songs of the old bards so passionately, and the old legends, which the emperor prized so much, how he used to read to him from the old gray parchment which he, Eginhard, had written so carefully, how his own favourite dark-eyed daughter had so often been present, sitting at his feet listening intently to the reader — all this came back to his memory, saddening his heart, and filling his eyes with tears.

V.

Bugle-horns sounded through the forest, Charles and his followers were at the chase. The old emperor, seeking to forget his grief, had seized his spear and had gone out to hunt.

In his eagerness to follow a magnificent stag he had become separated from his escort. The sun was already low in the west; the animal, now seeing no way of escape, as his pursuer was close behind him, dashed into a river and swam to the other side. The emperor, in hot pursuit and much exhausted, arrived at the water's edge, and for the first time noticed that he was alone, and in a part of the country quite unknown to him.

The river lay before him and the forest behind, but the latter seemed to be quite impenetrable. It was already night, and Charles sought in vain to find some path or track.

As he was looking round him, he perceived a light in the distance. Greatly pleased he started off in that direction, and found a little hut close to the river, but on looking through the window Charlemagne saw that the room was a very poor one.

"Perhaps this is the hermitage of some pious man," thought he, and knocked at the door, whereupon a fair haired man appeared on the threshold.

Without mentioning his name, the emperor informed him what had happened, and begged shelter for the night.

At the sound of this loved voice, the man trembled, but controlling himself, he invited the emperor to enter. A young woman was sitting on a stool rocking a baby in her arms. She started, became very pale at the sight of the emperor, and then hurried into the next room to hide her emotion; Charles sat down, and refusing refreshment from his host leaned his head wearily on his hands.

Minutes passed, and still he sat there lost in thought, dreaming of those happy by-gone days.

At last the sweet prattle of a child roused him, and looking up he saw a little girl about five years old at his side, stretching out her arms to him, bidding him good-night. Charles looked closely at the little angel-like creature, his heart throbbing within him. "What is your name, little one?" asked he. "Emma," answered the child.

"Emma," repeated Charles with tears in his eyes, and drawing the child closer to him he pressed a kiss on its forehead.

In a moment the man and his young wife were at the emperor's feet imploring pardon. "Emma! Eginhard!" cried he with great emotion, embracing them both. "Blessed be the place where I have found you again!"

Emma and Eginhard returned in great pomp to the emperor's court. The latter gave them his beautiful palace at Ingelheim, and only felt himself happy when he was with them.

He caused a cloister to be built on the spot where he had found them again, which, to the present day is called "Seligenstadt," "town of the happy."

In the church belonging to this little town the tomb of Eginhard and Emma is still shown, for according to their wishes, their bones were interred in the same coffin.

Rüdesheim
The Brömserburg

•

In the lofty cathedral of Spires stood
a great assemblage of knights, and on the
throne near the altar sat Conrad der
Staufe with his hands resting on the hilt
of his sword. All were listening intently
to the burning words of Bernard of Clairvaux who was describing the ruthless
manner in which the holy places of Palestine had been laid waste. As the saintly
preacher ended with a thrilling appeal to
the religious feelings of his audience, a
great shout, "On, to Jerusalem!" rang
through the sacred edifice. Most of the
knights offered to bring as many followers as possible to aid their pious Emperor. Among those present was Hans
Brömser, the lord of the Niederburg at
Rüdesheim. This noble knight, the last

of his race, was not detained at home by family cares. His wife had early been taken from him by death, and Mechtildis, the only offspring of their marriage, was left under the protection of the neighbouring Falkenstein family.

So the pious warriors marched by devious and dangerous routes to that land where Our Lord lived and suffered. In fierce battle with the Saracens many a noble knight closed his eyes forever. Many met a harder fate — a living death in the noisome prisons of the unbelievers. After a lost battle Sir Brömser fell into the hands of the Turks, and in a dungeon had to suffer shameful imprisonment. Sometimes they would force their knightly foe to turn a millstone, while the crowd jeered. Then, in the hour of deepest misery the knight made a vow to God. "Give me my freedom again, and I vow that my child Mechtildis shall devote her life to the Church." And he repeated the solemn words again, and yet a third time.

Then happened what none of his companions in-arms had ever hoped for. The brave crusaders stormed this Turkish stronghold in the Syrian desert, and liberated their fellow-crusaders from captivity. Full of gratitude to God, Hans Brömser again fought valiantly in the holy cause.

Meanwhile at home in the hospitable keep above the Rhine a maiden awaited with anxiety the return of her father. Often in the silent hours, with sweetness and sunshine around her, without and within, she stood on the castle-wall and she saw in reverie that blue eastern land, whilst she listened, to the wild throbbing of her young heart in which the blossoms of first love were bursting.

Then one night her father returned to the Rhineland.

In the moss-covered courtyard of the castle Mechtildis embraced her father long and silently. Beside the maiden, now in her seventeenth year, stood the young lord of Falkenstein. The youth bowed deeply to the lord of the Brömserburg, and greeted him kindly with the words,

Charlemagne

"Welcome home, father!" Then the vow made in the Syrian prison rose like a spectre to pall the joy of the crusader's return.

In the banqueting hall of the castle a large company had assembled to celebrate the happy return of Hans Brömser and his faithful companions. The praise of the crusaders resounded and many stories were told of the dangers the heroes had encountered. With stirring words the knight related to his listening guests how he himself had fought in the sacred cause, and how he had suffered imprisonment among the heathen. Then in a lower tone, and with solemn words, he told his friends of the vow he had made in his hour of deep despair in the Syrian dungeon.

The painful silence which followed was broken by a stifled cry, and the knight's daughter, pale as the covering on the festive board, sank unconscious to the floor. With burning cheek and flashing eye the young lord of Falkenstein rose, and with a firm voice exclaimed, "Mechtildis belongs to me; she has solemnly given herself to me forever". The murmur soon subsided before the stern countenance of the lord of the castle. "Mechtildis has been dedicated to heaven, not to you, boy. The last of the Brömser race has sworn it, and abides by it". The knight said this with suppressed fury, and soon his guests departed in silence.

Mechtildis lay in her chamber in wild grief. The flickering lamp beside the crucifix threw an unsteady light on the extended form of the maiden who was measuring the tedious night hours in the love-anguish of her young heart. To the distracted maid her chamber seemed to be transformed to an oppressive dungeon. Seizing the lamp with a trembling hand she hurried up the narrow winding stair on to the roof of the castle, and there committed her great grief to the listening ear of night. Leaning on the wall, she looked away towards the castle where lived the noble young lord to whom she had dedicated her life. "I am thine, my beloved," she sob-bed. No star was visible in the sky. A wild autumn wind shrieked and swirled round the keep in accompaniment to the storm in the maiden's breast. A short piercing cry echoed in the darkness. Was it the bride of the winds or a human cry? The night swallowed it. From the parapet of the Brömserburg a female form had been hurled down into the dark floods of the Rhine below.

A bright harvest morning followed a stormy night. In the Brömserburg they were searching everywhere in vain for their lord's daughter. Soon however a mournful procession approached bearing the mortal remains of Mechtildis. In the early dawn a young woman had rescued the body from the waters of the river. Now the walls of the Brömserburg echoed with sounds of woe over the early death of this last fair young flower of the Brömser race. Hans Brömser threw himself on the body and buried his stern features in the snowy linen. Not a tear bedewed his eyelids.

As a propitiatory offering for the rest of the soul of the maiden who had thus avoided the monastic life, the knight in his deep sorrow vowed to build a chapel on the hill opposite his castle. Then Hans Brömser shut himself up in his chamber, and passed the following days in silent grief, while the grave closed over his wretched child.

Many months passed, but still not a stone of the promised chapel had been set up. In the bitterness of his sorrow the grief-stricken father had separated himself more and more from the world, and now brooded in gloomy isolation. One day a servant came before him with a likeness of the Mother of God which an ox had scraped up while ploughing a field on the hill opposite the castle, and three times the servant declared he had heard the "Not Gottes" (Suffering of God) called out. Then Hans Brömser remembered his vow, and the chapel for the peace of the soul of Mechtildis was erected. "Not Gottes" it is called to this day.

Bingen

The Mouse-Tower

*

Below Bingen in the middle of the Rhine there is a lonely island on which a stronghold is to be seen. This tower is called "the Mouse-Tower". For many centuries a very gloomy tale has been told about it in connection with Hatto, Archbishop of Mayence, whose evil deeds were well-known throughout the country.

Hatto is said to have been ambitious, heartless, and perfidious, as well as cruel towards the poor. He extorted taxes from his people, tolls were imposed, and new burdens invented only to gratify his haughty pride and his love of display. On a little island between Bingen and Rüdesheim he caused a tower to be built, so that all passing ships could be

44

stopped in the narrow passage, where they were obliged to pay toll.

Soon after the building of this custom-house there was a very bad harvest in the country round Mayence. Drought had parched the fields, and the little seed remaining had been destroyed by hail. The scarcity was felt all the more, because the bishop had bought up all the stores of corn that were left from the year before, and had stored them up safely in his granaries.

A terrible famine now threatened the land, spreading misery among the poor. The unhappy people implored the cruel bishop to lower the price of the corn in his store-house, which he wished to sell at such exorbitant prices that his subjects could not buy it. All their petitions were in vain. His advisers besought him to have pity on the deplorable condition of the poor, but Hatto remained unmoved. When cries of distress and the murmuring voices of the exasperated folk were raised against their hard-hearted master, the bishop gave free vent to the wicked thoughts of his soul.

One day a troop of hungry beggars came crowding to the episcopal palace crying for food. Hatto and his guests were just sitting down to a luxurious banquet. The bishop had been talking to his companions of these wretched people, and had expressed his opinion that it would be a good thing to do away with them altogether in some drastic way.

As the ragged mob of men, women, and children, with hollow cheeks and pale faces threw themselves at his feet crying for bread, a still more fiendish plan suggested itself. Beckoning to them with hypocritical kindness he promised them corn, and caused them to be led outside the town to a barn, where each one was to receive as much corn as he wished. The unhappy folk hurried forth, their hearts full of gratitude; but when they were all in the barn, Hatto ordered the doors to be locked and the barn to be set on fire.

The screams of the poor wretches were heartrending, and could be heard even in the bishop's palace.

But cruel Hatto called out scornfully to his advisers, "Listen! how the mice are squeaking among the corn. This eternal begging is at an end at last. May the mice bite me if it is not true!"

But the punishment which Heaven sent him was terrible. Thousands of mice came out of the burning barn, made their way to the palace, filled every chamber and corner, and at last attacked the bishop himself. His servants killed them by hundreds, but their numbers seemed only to increase, as did their ferocity also. The bishop was seized with horror and, anticipating God's punishment, he fled from the town and went on board a boat hoping to defend himself from his terrible pursuers. But the innumerable horde swam in legions after him, and when he reached his tower on the island thinking at least he would be safe there, the mice followed him, gnawing the tower and tearing for themselves an entrance with their sharp teeth, till at last they reached him whom they sought. The cruel man was devoured by the mice, which attacked him by scores. In his despair he offered his soul to the Evil One, if he would release his body from such awful agony. The Evil Spirit came, freed his body, but took his soul away for himself.

Thus runs the legend. History however speaks less severely of Hatto, the imperious prelate.

————

His great ambition was his desire of power. He was the founder of the temporal power which the seat of Mayence obtained, and which later on made it the first bishopric of the kingdom, but he was always hated by the citizens, who suffered much owing to his proud, despotic character.

It is true that he was the founder of the toll which ships in olden times were obliged to pay on the Rhine, so that this fact and many other cruel exactions of him, have helped to evolve the terrible legend of the Mouse-Tower.

St. Goar

Lorelei

*

Above Coblentz where the Rhine flows through hills covered with vineyards, there is a steep rock, round which many a legend has been woven — the Lurlei Rock. The boatman gazes up at its gigantic summit with awful reverence when his boat glides over the waters at twilight. Like chattering children the restless waves whisper round the rock, telling wonderful tales of its doings. Above on its gray head, the legend relates that a beautiful but false nymph, clothed in white with a wreath of stars in her flowing hair, used to sit and sing sweet songs, until a sad tragedy drove her forever away.

Long long ago, when night in her dark garment descended from the hills, and her silent comrade, the pale moon, cast a silver bridge over the deep green stream the soft voice of a woman was heard from the rock, and a creature of divine beauty was seen on its summit. Her golden locks flowed like a queenly mantle from her graceful shoulders, covering her snowwhite raiment so that her tenderly-formed body appeared like a cloud of light. Woe to the boatman who passed the rock at the close of day! As of old, men were fascinated by the heavenly song of the Grecian hero, so was the unhappy voyager allured by this being to sweet forgetfulness, his eyes, even as his soul, would be dazzled, and he could no longer steer clear of reefs and cliffs, and this beautiful siren only drew him to an early grave. Forgetting all else, he would steer towards her, already dreaming of having reached her; but the jealous waves would wash round his boat and at last dash him treacherously against the rocks. The roaring waters of the Rhine would drown the cries of agony of the victim who would never be seen again.

But the virgin to whom no one had ever approached, continued every night to sing soft and low, till darkness vanished in the first rays of light, and the great star of day drove the gray mists from the valley.

II.

Ronald was a proud youth and the boldest warrior at the court of his father, the Palatinate Count. He heard of this divine, enchanting creature, and his heart burned with the desire to behold her. Before having seen the waternymph, he felt drawn to her by an irresistible power.

Under pretence of hunting, he left the court, and succeeded in getting an old sailor to row him to the rock. Twilight was brooding over the valley of the Rhine when the boat approached the gigantic

4*

cliff; the departing sun had long sunk below the mountains, and now night was creeping on in silence; the evening star was twinkling in the deep blue firmament. Was it his protecting-angel who had placed it there as a warning to the deluded young man?

He gazed at it in rapture for some time, until a low cry from the old man at his side interrupted him. "The Lorelei!" whispered he, startled, "do you see her — the enchantress?" The only answer was a soft murmur which escaped from the youth. With wide-open eyes he looked up and lo! there she was. Yes, this was she, this wonderful creature! A glorious picture in a dark frame. Yes, that was her golden hair, and those were her flowing white garments.

She was hovering up above on the rocks combing her beautiful hair; rays of light surrounded her graceful head, revealing her charms in spite of the night and the distance, and as he gazed, her lips opened, and a song thrilled through the silence, soft and plaintive like the sweet notes of a nightingale on a still summer evening.

From her height she looked down into the hazy distance and cast at the youth a rapturous look which sank down into his soul, thrilling his whole frame.

His eyes were fixed on the features of this celestial being where he read the sweet story of love . . . Rocks, stream, glorious night, all melted into a mist before his eyes, he saw nothing but the figure above, nothing but her radiant eyes. The boat crept along, too slowly for him, he could no longer remain in it, and if his ear did not deceive him, this creature seemed to whisper his name with unutterable sweetness, and calling to her, he dashed into the water.

A death-like cry echoed from the rocks . . . . and the waves sighed and washed over the unhappy youth's corpse.

The old boatman moaned and crossed himself, and as he did so, lightning tore the clouds asunder, and a loud peal of thunder was heard over the mountains. Then the waves whispered gently below, and again from the heights above, sad and dying away, sounded the Lurlei's song.

III.

The sad news was soon brought to the Palatinate Count, who was overpowered with grief and anger. He ordered the false enchantress to be delivered up to him, dead or alive.

The next day a boat sailed down the Rhine, manned by four hardy bold warriors. The leader looked up sternly at the great rocks which seemed to be smiling silently down at him. He had asked permission to dash the diabolical seducer from the top of the rocks into the foaming whirlpool below, where she would find a certain death, and the count had readily agreed to this plan of revenge.

IV.

The first shades of twilight were gliding softly over mountain and hill.

The rock was surrounded by armed men, and the leader, followed by some daring comrades, was climbing up the side of the mountain the top of which was veiled in a golden mist, which the men thought were the last rays of sunset. It was a bright gleam of light enshrouding the nymph who appeared on the rocks, dreamingly combing her golden hair. She then took a string of pearls from her bosom, and with her slender white hand bound them round her forehead. She cast a mocking glance at the threadening men approaching her.

"What are the weak sons of the earth seeking up here on the heights?" said she, moving her rosy lips scornfully. "You sorceress!" cried the leader enraged, adding with a contemptuous smile, "You! We shall dash you down into the river below!"

An echoing laugh was heard over the mountain.

"Oh! the Rhine will come himself to fetch me!" cried the maiden.

Then bending her slender body over the precipice yawning below, she tore the jewels from her forehead, hurling them triumphantly into the waters, while in a low sweet voice she sang: —

"Haste thee, haste thee oh father dear!
Send forth thy steeds from the waters clear.
I will ride with the waves and the wind!"

Then a storm burst forth, the Rhine rose, covering its banks with foam. Two gigantic billows like snow-white steeds rose out of the depths, and carried the nymph down into the rushing current.

V.

The terrified messengers returned to the count, bringing him the tidings of this wonderful event.

Ronald, whose body a chance wave had washed up on the banks of the river, was deeply mourned throughout the country.

From this time forth, the Lorelei was never seen again. Only when night sheds her dark shadow on the hills, and the

Siegfried murdered by Hagen

pale moon weaves a silver bridge over the deep green stream, then the voice of a woman, soft and low, is heard echoing from the weird heights of the rocks.

— — —

The Lorelei has vanished, but her charm still remains.

Thou canst find it, O Wanderer, in the eyes of the maidens near the Rhine. It blooms on their cheeks, it lingers on their rosy lips, there thou wilt find its traces.

Arm thy heart, steel thy will, blindfold thine eye!

As a poet of the Rhine once wisely and warningly sang, "My son, my son, beware of the Rhine . . ."

The Lorelei has vanished, but her charm still remains.

Sterrenberg
and Liebenstein

The Brothers

*

I.

In the middle ages, an old knight belonging to the court of the Emperor Conrad II. lived in a castle called Sterrenberg, near Boppard. The old warrior had two sons left to him. His wife had died many years before, and since her death, merry laughter had seldom been heard in the halls of the beautiful castle.

Soon a ray of sunshine seemed to break into these solemn rooms; a distant cousin at Rüdesheim had died, leaving his only child, a beautiful young girl, to the care of his relative.

The golden-haired Angela became the

pet of the castle, and won the affection and friendship of the two sons by her engaging ways. What had already happened hundred of times now happened among these young people, love replaced the friendship of the two young knights, and both tried to win the maiden's favour.

The old master of the castle noticed this change, and his father's heart forebode trouble.

Both sons were equally dear to him, but perhaps his first born, who had inherited his mother's gentle character, fulfilled his heart's desire more than the fiery spirit of Conrad the younger.

From the first moment when the orphan appeared at his family seat, he had conceived the thought that his favourite son Henry, who was heir to his name and estates, would marry the maiden.

Henry loved Angela with a profound, sincere feeling which he seldom expressed.

His brother, on the contrary, made no secret of his ardent love, and soon the old man perceived with sorrow that the beautiful girl returned his younger son's passionate love. Henry, too, was not unaware of the happiness of this pair, and in generous self-denial he tried to bury his grief, and to rejoice heartily in his brother's success.

The distress of the elder brother did not escape Angela. She was much moved when she first remarked that his voice trembled on pronouncing her name, but soon love dazzled her eyes, so that the clouds on his troubled countenance passed unnoticed by her.

About this time St. Bernhard of Clairvaux came from France to the Rhine, preaching a second crusade against the Infidels. The fiery words of the saintly monk roused many thousands to action; his appeal likewise reached the castle of Sterrenberg.

Henry, though not envying his brother's happiness, felt that it would be impossible for him to be a constant witness of it, and thus he was glad to answer this call, and to take up the cross.

Conrad, too, longing for action and dominated by the impulse of the moment, was stirred up by the witching charms which a crusade to Palestine offered. His adventurous soul, cramped up in this castle so far removed from the world, thirsted for the adventures, which he imagined were awaiting the crusaders in the far off East. In vain the tears and prayers of the young girl were shed, in vain was the sorrow of his father who begged him not to desert him.

The old man was in despair about the unbending resolutions of his sons.

"Who will remain at the castle of my forefathers, if you both abandon it now, perhaps never to return," cried he sorrowfully. "I implore you, my eldest son, you, the very image of your mother, to have pity on your father's gray hairs. And you, Conrad, have pity on the tears of your betrothed." The brothers remained silent. Then the eldest grasped the old man's hand, saying gently.

"I shall not leave you, my father."

"And you, Angela," said the younger to the weeping maiden, "you will try and bear this separation, and will plant a sprig of laurel to make a wreath for me when I return."

II.

The next day the young knight left the home of his forefathers. At first the maiden seemed inconsolable in her grief. But soon her love began to slumber like a tired child; on awakening from this drowsiness indignation seized her, whispering complainingly in her ear, and disturbing all the sweet memories in which the picture of her light-hearted lover gleamed forth, he who had parted from her for the sake of empty glory.

Now left to herself, she began to consider the proud youth who was forced to live under the same roof with his rejected love. She admired his good qualities which all seemed to have escaped her before, his great daring at the chase, his skill with weapons, and his many kind acts of pure friendship to her, with the view of sweetening the bitter separation from which she was suffering.

He seemed afraid of rousing the love which was still sleeping in his heart.

In the meantime Angela felt herself drawn more and more towards the knight; she wished to try and make him understand that her love for his younger brother had only been a youthful passion, which seemed to have flown when he left her. She felt unhappy when she understood that Henry, whom she now began really to love, seemed to feel nothing but brotherly affection for her, and she longed in her inmost soul for a word of love from him.

Henry was not unaware of this change in her affections, but he proudly smothered every rising thought in his heart for his brother's betrothed.

The old knight was greatly pleased

when, one day, Angela came to him, and with tears in her eyes disclosed to him the secret of her heart.

He prayed God fervently to bring these two loving hearts together whom he believed were destined for one another by will of God. In his dreams he already saw Angela in her castle like his dead wife and his first-born son, rocking her little baby, a blue-eyed, fair-haired child. Then he would suddenly recollect his impetuous younger son fighting in the crusades, and his dreams would be hastily interrupted.

Just opposite to his ancestral hall he caused a proud fort to be built, and called it "Liebenstein", intending it for his second son when he returned from the Holy Land. The castle was hardly finished, when the old man died.

The crusade at last was at an end. All the knights from the Rhine country brought back the news with them on their return from the Holy Land, that Conrad had married a beautiful Grecian woman in the East, and was now on his way home with her.

Henry was beside himself with wrath on hearing this news. Such dishonourable conduct and shameful neglect seemed impossible to him, and going to the maiden he informed her of his brother's approaching return.

She turned very pale, her lips moved, but her tongue found no words.

III.

A large ship was seen one day sailing along the Rhine with strange flags waving on its masts. Angela saw it from her tower where she now spent many a long day reflecting on her unfortunate destiny, and she hastily called up the elder brother.

The ship approached nearer and nearer. Soon the cries of the boatmen could be heard, and the faces of the crew could be distinguished.

Suddenly the maiden uttered a cry, and

threw herself weeping into the arms of the knight. The latter gazed at the vessel, his brows contracted. Yes! there on board, in shining armour, stood his brother, with a beautiful strange woman clinging to his arm.

The ship touched land. One of the first, Conrad sprang on shore. The two watchers in the tower disappeared. A man approached Conrad and informed him that the new castle was destined for him. The same day the impetuous knight sent notice of his arrival to Sterrenberg castle, but his brother answered him, that he would wait for him on the bridge, but would only meet sword in hand the faithless lover who had deserted his betrothed.

Twilight was creeping over the two castles. On the narrow ground separating the forts the brothers strove together in a deadly fight.

They were equally courageous, equally strong those two opponents, and their swords crossed swiftly, one in righteous anger, the other in wounded pride. But soon the elder received a blow, and the blood began to drop on his breastplate.

The bushes were at this moment suddenly pushed asunder, and a maiden, veiled in white, dashed in between the fighters thrusting them from each other. It was Angela, who cried out in a despairing voice:

"In God's name stop! and for your father's sake cease, ere it be too late. She for whom you have drawn your swords, is now going to take the veil, and will beg God day and night to forgive you, Conrad, for your falseness, and will pray Him to bless you and your brother for ever."

Both brothers threw down their arms. Conrad, his head deeply bowed, covered his face with his hand. He did not dare to look at the maiden who stood there, a silent reproach to him. Henry took the weeping girl's hand.

"Come sister," said he, "such faithlessness does not deserve your tears."

They disappeared among the trees.

Silently Conrad stood gazing after them. A feeling which he had never known seemed to rise up in his heart, and, bending his head, he wept bitterly.

IV.

The cloister, Marienburg, lay in a valley at some distance from the castles, and there Angela found peace. A wall was soon built up between the two forts Sterrenberg and Liebenstein, a silent witness of the enmity between the two brothers.

Banquet followed banquet in the newly built castle, and the beautiful Grecian won great triumphs among the knights of the Rhine.

But sorrow seemed to have taken possession of Sterrenberg castle. Henry had not wished to move the maiden from her purpose, but from the time of her departure, his strength faded away. At the foot of the mountain he caused a cloister to be built, and a few months later he passed away from this world, just on the same day that the bells were tolling for Angela's death.

The lord of Liebenstein was not granted a lasting happiness with his beautiful wife. She fled with a knight who had long enjoyed the lavish hospitality at castle Liebenstein. Conrad, overcome by sorrow and disgrace, threw himself from a pinnacle of the castle into the depths below.

The strongholds then fell into the hands of Knight Brömser of Rüdesheim, and since that time have fallen into ruins. The church and cloister still remain in the valley, and are the scene of many a pilgrimage.

Andernach

Genovefa

*

I.

In all the Rhine provinces the virtuous spouse of Count Siegfried of the Palatinate was esteemed and venerated. The people called her St. Genovefa, which name indeed she was worthy of, as she suffered cruel trials and sorrows. Siegfried's castle stood near the old town of Andernach, just at the time when Charles Martel was reigning over the Franks.

Siegfried and his young wife lived in peaceful unity, till a cloud came over their happiness. The much-dreaded Arabs from Spain had forced their way into Gaul, and were now marching northwards, burning and destroying all on their course. The enemies of the cross must be repuls-

71

ed, unless the west was to share the fate of Africa, which had been subdued by the Mohametans.

The war-cry reached the Palatinate, and Siegfried had to go forth to the fight. Equipped in his armour, and having kissed his weeping wife, he bade farewell to the castle of his fathers. But he was sad at heart at leaving the spot where the happiest days of his life had been spent. He entrusted the administration of his property to Golo, his steward, and recommended his beloved wife very earnestly to his protection, begging her in turn to trust him in everything.

The poor countess was heart-broken at this bitter separation. She felt the loneliness of the castle deeply, she longed for his happy presence and the sound of his voice. She could never speak to Golo as to the friend to whose care her husband had recommended her. Her pure eyes shrank from the passionate look which gleamed in his. It seemed to her that he followed her every movement with a look which her childlike soul did not understand.

She missed her husband's presence more and more. She would go out on the balcony and weave golden dreams, and while she sat there, looking out over the hazy blue distance, she longed for the moment when Siegfried would return, when she could lean her head upon his breast, and tell him of the great happiness in store for them.

Perhaps the war against the heathens might last so long that she would be able to hold the pledge of their love joyfully out to him from the balcony on his return. And the countess' lovely face would be lit up with a gleam of blissful happiness, and she would while away the time on her favourite spot, dreaming and looking out into the hazy blue distance.

The secret aversion which the countess felt towards the steward was not without a reason. Her angel-like beauty had awakened lustful passion in Golo's breast, which he did not strive to hide. On the contrary his frequent intercourse with her, who was as gracious to him as to all her other inferiors, stirred his passion still more, and one day, losing all control, he threw himself at the countess' feet, declaring his love for her, and imploring her to return it. Genovefa was horrified at this confession. With indignation and scorn she rejected his love, forbidding him to appear before her as he had utterly forgotten his duty, and at the same time, threatening to complain of him to her husband. Golo's eyes flared up, and a deadly look of hatred gleamed from them.

He could hope for no pardon from his angry mistress. Besides, his pride would not allow him to seek it, and now his one desire was revenge. It only remained for him to follow his dastardly plan and to avoid Siegfried's wrath.

Hatred raged in his breast. He dismissed all the servants of the castle and put new ones of his own creation in their places. Then one day he appeared before the horrified countess, and openly

The Lorelei

accused her of being unfaithful to her husband far away.

Shame and wrath robbed Genovefa of speech. Golo explained to the servants who were standing around in silent amazement, that he had already informed the count of his wife's faithless conduct, and that he, Golo, as present administrator of the castle, now condemned the countess to be imprisoned in the dungeon.

The unhappy Genovefa awakened to find herself in an underground cell of the castle. She covered her face in deep sorrow, imploring Him who had sent her this trial, to help her in her present affliction. There after some time a son was born to her. She baptized him with her tears, giving him the name of Tristan, which means "full of sorrows."

II.

Siegfried had already been absent six months. He had fought like a hero in many a desperate battle. The fanatical followers of Mohamet having crossed the Pyrenees, struggled with wild enthusiasm, hoping to subdue the rest of western Europe to the doctrines of Islam by fire and sword. In several encounters, the Franks had been obliged to give way to their power. These unbridled hordes had already penetrated into the heart of Gaul, when Charles first appeared and engaged the Arabs in the bloody battle of Tours. From morning till evening the struggle on which hung the fate of Europe raged. And there Charles proved himself worthy of the name of Martel "the hammer", which he afterwards received.

Siegfried fought at the leader's side like a lion; but towards evening a Saracen's lance pierced him, and though the wound was not mortal, yet he was obliged to remain inactive for several months on a sick-bed, where he thought with longing in his heart of his loving wife by the Rhine.

A messenger arrived one day at the camp bearing a parchment from Golo,

Siegfried's steward. The count gazed long at the fateful letter, trying to comprehend its meaning. What he had read, ran thus: "Your wife is unfaithful to you and has betrayed you for the sake of Drago, a servant, who ran away." The hero crushed the letter furiously in his hand, a groan escaping from his white lips. Then he started off accompanied by a few followers, and rode towards the Ardennes, never stopping till he reached his own fort. A man stood on the balcony, looking searchingly out into the distance, and seeing a cloud of dust approaching in which a group of horsemen soon became visible, his eyes gleamed triumphantly.

A stately knight advanced, his charger stamping threateningly on the drawbridge. Golo, with hypocritical emotion stood before the count, who had now alighted from his foaming horse, and informed him again of what had happened. "Where is the evil-doer who has stained the honour of my house, where is he, that I may crush his life out?" cried Siegfried in a fury.

"My lord, I have punished the wretch deservedly and lashed him out of the castle," answered Golo in a stern voice, sighing deeply.

The count made a sign to Golo whose false eyes gleamed with devilish joy, to lead the way.

Siegfried **entered** the dungeon, followed by his servants and also by those who had travelled with him. Genovefa listened breathlessly in her prison, with a loved name trembling on her lips and a prayer to God in her heart. Now the terrible trial would come to an end, now she would leave this dungeon of disgrace triumphantly, and exchange the crown of thorns for the victor's wreath.

The bolt was unfastened, firm steps and men's voices were heard, the iron doors were dashed open. She snatched her slumbering child, the pledge of their love, and held it towards her dear husband. His name was on her lips, but before she could utter it, a cry of agony escaped her. He had cast her from him and, his accusations falling like blows from a hammer on her head, the poor innocent countess fell senseless to the ground. The next day two servants lead mother and child out into the forest, where with their own hands, they were to kill her who had been so unfaithful to her husband, and her child also. They were to bring back two tongues to the count as a proof that they had obeyed his orders.

The servants drove them into the wildest dephts of the forest where only the screams of birds of prey broke the silence. They drew their knives. But the poor countess fell on her knees, and holding up her little child, implored them to spare their lives, if not for her sake, at least for the sake of the helpless child. Pity entered the two men's hearts and withheld their hands. Dragging the mother and child still deeper into the forest, they turned away hastily, leaving their victims to themselves.

They brought two harts' tongues to the count, informing him that they had fulfilled his orders.

III.

Genovefa's tired feet wandered through the unknown forest, her child crying with hunger. She prayed fervently to Heaven in her despair, and tears were sent to relieve the dull pain in her heart, after which she felt more composed, and her child was soon sweetly slumbering. To her great astonishment she perceived a cavern near her, where she could take shelter, and as if God wished to show that He had heard her prayer, a white doe came towards the cavern, rubbing herself caressingly against the abandoned woman. Willingly the gentle animal allowed the little child to be suckled. The next day the doe came back again, and Genovefa thanked God from the depths of her heart. She found roots, berries, and plants, to support herself, and every day the tame doe came back to her, and at last remained always with her.

Days, weeks, and months passed. Her unfaltering faith had rendered her agony less. In time she learned to forgive her husband who had condemned her unjustly, and she even pardoned him who had taken such bitter revenge on her. Her lovely cheeks had become thinner, but the forest winds had breathed a soft red into them, and the child who had no cares nor gnawing pain in its heart, grew into a beautiful little boy.

IV.

At the castle on the Rhine, sorrow was a constant guest since this terrible event had happened. Siegfried's burning anger had sunk into sorrow, and often when he was wandering restlessly through the rooms so rich in sweet memories, where now a deserted stillness reigned, the agony awoke again in his heart. He now repented of his hastiness, and a voice whispered in his ear that he had been too severe in his cruel punishment, that he had condemned too quickly, and that he should have considered what he could have done to mitigate her punishment.

When these haunting voices pursued him, he would hurry away from the castle and its loneliness, not being able to bear the torment of his thoughts. Then to forget his trouble, he would follow the chase with the yelping hounds. But he only seldom succeeded in dulling his misery. Everywhere he seemed to see the pale face of a woman looking imploringly at him.

The state of his master's soul had not escaped Golo, and this crafty man cringed the more to the sorrowful count, feigning to care for his welfare. A starving person accepts even the bread which a beggar-man offers, and Siegfried, supposing his steward wished to compensate him for his loss, accepted willingly every proof of devotion, and recompensed him with his favour, at the same time hating the man in his inmost soul who had rendered him such a terrible service.

One day the count rode out to the chase, accompanied by only a few retainers, one of whom was Golo. Siegfried pressed deeper than was his custom into the forest. A milkwhite doe sprang up before him and sportsmanlike, he chased this singular animal through the bushes, hoping to shoot it. His spear had just grazed it, when it disappeared suddenly into a cavern. A woman whose ragged garments scarcely covered her nakedness, leading a little boy by the hand, suddenly came out of the opening in the rock, and the doe, seeking protection, rubbed herself against her. She looked at the hunter, but her limbs trembled so that she could scarcely stand, only her large sad eyes gazed wistfully at him. A stifled cry, half triumphant, half a groan, escaped from her lips, and she threw herself at the count's feet. From the voice which for long months had only moved in earnest prayer or in low sweet words to the child, now

flowed solemn protestations of her innocence. Her words burned like fire into the
soul of the count, and drawing her to his
breast, he kissed her tears, and then sank
at her feet imploring her pardon.

He pressed his little boy to his heart,
overcome with gratitude and happiness,
and wept with joy, calling him by a thousand affectionate names.

Then at the sound of his bugle-horn
his retinue hastened towards him, Goio
among them.

„Do you know these two?" thundered
out the count to the latter, tearing him
from the throng and conducting him to
Genovefa.

The wretch, as if struck by a club, broke
down and, clasping his master's knees,
he confessed his wickedness and begged
for mercy. Siegfried thrust him contemp-
tuously from him, refusing sternly, in
spite of the countess' intercession, to pardon his crime. Golo was bound and led
away, and a disgraceful death was his
reward.

Now began a time of great happiness for Siegfried and his saint-like wife, and they lived in undisturbed peace with their little son.

In gratitude to Heaven Siegfried caused a church to be built on the spot where the white doe had appeared to him first. The countess often made a pilgrimage to this house of God, to thank Him who had caused her tears to be turned into joy. Then a day came when her corpse was carried into the forest, and was buried in the church. Even now in Laach, the wanderer is shown the church and the tombstone, also the cavern where she suffered so much. Thus the name of St. Genovefa will last to all time.

Hammerstein

The old Knight and his Daughters

*

Above Rheinbrohl, on a dreary sandstone rock, stand the ruins of the old imperial fortress of Hammerstein. For a thousand years the storms have beat on those desolate walls. One of the first owners was Wolf von Hammerstein, a faithful vassal of the Emperor. It was Henry IV. who then ruled, and partly by his own faults, partly by those of others, the crown had indeed become to this sovereign one of thorns. Wolf of Hammerstein had made the historic pilgrimage to Canossa alone with his master. Now, on account of the infirmities of age the venerable knight seldom descended the

castle-hill, and only from afar, the loud
trumpet call of the world fell upon his
ears. His wife, now for several years
deceased, had born him six daughters,
all attractive maidens and tenderly attached
to their surviving parent, but their fil-
ial affection met with the roughest and
most ungrateful responses from the sour
old fellow. It was a sore grievance to
Wolf of Hammerstein that he had no son.
He would willingly have exchanged his
halfdozen daughters for a single male
heir. The girls were only too well aware
of this fact, and tried all the more, by constant love and tender care to reconcile
their ungracious parent to his lot.

One evening it thus befell. The autumn
wind grumbled round the castle like a
croaking raven, and the old knight, Wolf
of Hammerstein, sat by a cheerful fire and
peevishly nursed his gouty limbs. In spite
of the most assiduous attentions of his
daughters he remained in a most surly
mood. The pretty maidens however kept
hovering round the ill-tempered old fellow

like so many tender doves. Then the
porter announced two strangers. Both
were wrapped in their knightly mantles,
and in spite of his troubles the hospitable
lord of the castle prepared to welcome his
guests. Into the comfortable room two
shivering and weary travellers advanced,
and as outlaws they craved shelter and
protection for the night. At the sound of
one of the voices the knight started up,
listening eagerly, and when the stranger
raised his visor and threw back his mantle,
Wolf of Hammerstein sank on his knees
at the stranger's feet, and seizing his
hand he pressed it to his lips, exclaiming:
"Henry, my lord and king!" Then, with
trembling voice the Emperor told his old
comrade-in-arms that he was a fugitive,
and before one who had torn from him
the imperial crown and mantle. And when
the old knight, trembling with excitement,
demanded who this impious and dishonourable man might be, the Emperor murmured the words, "My son," and then
buried his face in his hands.

Rigid as a marble statue stood the old knight. Like a bolt from heaven the consciousness of his past ignoble conduct had flashed upon him. Suddenly he seemed to feel how tenderly the loving arms of his daughters had enfolded him. He spread out his hands towards them, as if anxious to atone by the tenderness of a minute for the harshness of years. Then the Emperor, deeply touched, thus addressed the old man. "Dear comrade-in arms, your position is indeed enviable. The faithful love of your daughters will tend you in your declining years. No misguided son, impatient for your end, will hunt you from your home. Alas, for me, to-morrow accompanied by a few faithful followers, I must go down to battle against my own flesh and blood."

Towards midnight the unhappy monarch was conducted to a room prepared with care for his reception; and, while he sank into a troubled sleep, the old knight overwhelmed his daughters with long-delayed caresses. In his heart, he silently

entreated for pardon for the deep grudge
he had long cherished against the God
who had been pleased to grant him no son.

Mayence

Heinrich Frauenlob

*

The priest or as some say, canon, in
the old town of Mayence was a very
worthy man, and at the same time a
heaven-gifted singer. Besides devoting
himself to science, he composed numerous
pious verses which he dedicated to the
Holy Virgin. He also played the harp, and
wrote many beautiful songs in honour
of the female sex.

In contrast to many contemporary
poets, he considered "woman" a higher
title than "wife" which only signifies a
married woman. So on account of the
chivalry displayed in his numberless poems

and songs, posterity gave him the name of „Frauenlob", under which title he is better known than under his own name of Heinrich of Meissen.

The love and veneration which thankful women paid him was very great, not only during his life-time, but even more so after his death. Their grief was intense when it became known that the poet's voice would never more be heard in this world. It was agreed to honour him with such a burial as no poet had ever before received. The funeral procession moved slowly and sorrowfully along the streets, the greater part of the cortege being women in deep mourning who prayed for the repose of the poet's soul. Eight of the most beautiful among them carried the coffin, which was covered with sweet-scented flowers.

At the grave songs of lamentation were heard from women's gentle voices. Precious Rhine-wine which had been the poet's favourite drink, and which so often had inspired his poetry, was poured by hands

The Brothers

of his admirers over his grave, so profusely, the legend relates, that the entrance of the church was flooded by the libation. But still more precious than all these gifts were the tears, which on this memorable day were shed by many a gentle lady.

The wanderer can still see the monument erected to this great benefactor in the cathedral at Mayence, which represents the figure of a beautiful woman in pure-white marble placing a wreath on the coffin of the great singer, who had honoured women in the most chivalrous of songs.

Bishop Willigis

In the year 1000 there was a very pious priest in Mayence called Bishop Willigis. He was only the son of a poor wheelwright, but by his perseverance and his own merit he had attained to the dignity of first priest of the kingdom. The honest citizens of Mayence loved and honoured the worthy divine, although they did not altogether like having to bow down to one who had been brought up in a simple cottage like themselves.

The bishop once reproved them in gentle tones for thinking too much of mere descent. This vexed the supercilious citizens, and one night they determined to play Willigis a trick. They took some chalk and drew enormous wheels on all the doors of his house.

Early next morning as the bishop was going to mass, he noticed the scoffers' malicious work. He stood silently looking at the wheels, the chaplain by his side expecting every moment that the reverend prelate would burst forth in a terrible rage. But a gay smile spread over the bishop's features, and ordering a painter to be sent to him, he told him to paint white wheels on a scarlet background, visible to every eye, just where the chalk wheels had been drawn, and underneath to paint the words, "Willigis! Willigis! just think what you have risen from." But he did not stop there. He ordered the wheelwright to make him a plough-wheel , and caused it to be placed over his couch in memory of his extraction.

Thereafter the scoffers were put to silence, and the people of Mayence began to honour and esteem their worthy bishop, who, though he had been so exalted, possessed such honest common-sense.

White wheels on a red ground have been the arms of the Bishops of Mayence ever since.

Assmannshausen

St. Clement's Chapel

＊

Rudolphus of Habsburg, elected emper-
or after the terrible anarchy which
had reigned in Germany when the land
was left without a ruler, determined by
firm and vigorous government, to put an
end to the evil-doings of the robber-
knights who held sway along the Rhine.
He had already threatened these much-
dreaded nobles who disturbed the peace
of the country and the government of its
ruler, and now hearing that they still
continued their ravages, the emperor appeared himself in the Rhine countries, resolved to annihilate them and to destroy
their strongholds.
On his way through the land, Rudol-

phus set fire to all the strongholds on the upper Rhine. The burning of the castles of Reichenstein, Sooneck, Heimburg and others, was an awful sight to the inhabitants of the valley below. Numerous members of these ancient noble races met the death of felons, and their bodies were hung up on trees as a warning to others.

Moaning and wailing were then heard throughout the land, mothers, wives, and daughters, weeping for their dead. On the other hand the merchants who had endured hardships and sufferings during these years, were now delighted with the stern justice dealt out by the emperor.

Under cover of darkness stealthy forms could be seen creeping to the place of execution, and silently and mournfully taking away the bodies of their relatives to preserve them from ignominious destruction. They then buried the wretched remains in consecrated ground, hoping thus to satisfy the fears which haunted them of future punishment, for many of their dear ones had stained their swords with the blood of their neighbours.

In order to atone for these sins, and in accordance with the wise counsel of a priest, the trees on which the bodies had been hanged were cut down, and the wood used to build a chapel of expiation. Stones were also taken from the smoking ruins of the burning castles and employed for the same purpose. The little church was built on the lonely place of execution on the Rhine near Assmannshausen.

The day arrived — a day of great sorrow and weeping — when all was ready, and the priest was to read prayers from the altar for the first time. Many funeral barges were to be seen on the river, bringing the dead.

The Archbishop of Mayence absolved the bodies from their sins, and afterwards they were all interred together near the little church for the second time.

This occurred towards the end of the thirteenth century. For long years afterwards prayers were offered up in this church in Assmannshausen for the souls of the dead.

The once proud and mighty races gradually died out, and their strongholds fell into ruins. And time which had demolished the castles on the heights above, began her work of destruction on the little church below; its roof decayed and its walls crumbled.

The ancient little church of St. Clement has since that time been raised again from its ruins, and now the voice of God's priest is heard chanting in it again, as it was heard six hundred years ago.

Castle Rheinstein

The Wooing

*

In Castle Rheinstein once lived a knight called Diethelm, who devoted himself without restraint to all the excesses of the robber barons. From one of his pillaging expeditions he brought back a charming maiden called Jutta. As the delicate ivy twines itself round the rough oak and clothes its knotty stem with shimmering velvet, so in time the gentle conduct of this maiden changed the coarse baron to a noble knight who eschewed pillaging and carousing, and ultimately made the fair Jutta the honoured wife of her captor.

The first fruit of their love cost the tender mother her life. Gerda however, who much resembled her mother, grew to such a noble beauty that soon wooers from

far and near came to sue for the hand
of the beautiful daughter of the aged
Diethelm. But the aged knight made a
most careful selection, and many gay
wooers had to depart in sorrow. One
young man was however regarded fa-
vourably by the maid, and not unkindly
looked upon by the old man. He was the
oldest son of the owner of the Sternburg.
This young man had contrived to win the
maiden's heart, and one day, while Gerda
presided as queen of love and beauty at
a tournament held in the courtyard of
Castle Rheinstein, Helmbrecht made an
avowal of his love.

Some days thereafter the young lord
according to courtly fashion appointed
his uncle Gunzelin of Reichenstein to woo
his chosen bride for him. But Gunzelin
though an old man was full of knavery
and falsehood, and so instead of wooing
for his nephew he ingratiated himself with
Gerda's father. Moreover, as the old knight
was descended from an ancient family
and possessed of much wealth Diethelm

102

was easily induced to promise him the hand of the fair Gerda. To the astonishment of this worthy pair Gerda would not listen to the suit of her rich wooer. Her heart belonged to the nephew, not the uncle. Now Count Diethelm was aroused, and with the blind fury of his earlier years swore to his rich companion that Gerda belonged to him, and should never wed the young cocksparrow of the Sternburg.

In her quiet chamber the unhappy maid wept out her heart's grief, but burning tears did not thaw the ice-cold heart of the father. In vain the young lover tried to gain the old knight's favour, but Diethelm merely referred to his knightly word solemnly pledged to the lord of Reichenstein.

Soon the day approached on which Gunzelin, with the smiling self satisfaction of an old roué, and decked out to give himself all the appearance of young manhood, was to lead the fairest maiden in the Rhineland to his stately castle. Gerda

who possessed the mild disposition of her
deceased mother had submitted to the
inevitable. On a bright summer morning
the bridal procession started from the
courtyard of Castle Rheinstein, and moved
towards the Clement's Chapel situated
in the neighbourhood. Horns blew and
trumpets sounded. On a milk-white palfrey, sat the fair young bride, deadly
pale. She was thinking of her absent lover
who in this hour must be enduring the
greatest anguish on her account. Then all
at once a swarm of buzzing gadflies came
out of the bush and fastened fiercely on
the palfrey which bore the fair Gerda.
The animal reared and broke from the
bridal procession. Boldly the bridegroom
on his grandly caparisoned steed dashed
forward to check the frightened animal,
but his war-horse missing its footing on
the narrow bridle path fell over a precipice
carrying its master with it. The dying
knight was carried by the wedding-guests
back to Castle Rheinstein. The aged Diethelm was also unfortunate in his attempt

to stop the runaway steed. The maddened animal had struck him on the shin-bone, and wounded him. The servants were thus obliged to carry the moaning grey-beard back to his castle as speedily and carefully as possible. The surgeon had a sad time of it during the next week as he attended to the enraged old knight's wounds and bruises.

When the runaway horse had disappeared round a bend of the path a man threw himself upon it, and bringing the trembling animal to a standstill clasped the unconscious bride in his arms. Helmbrecht, concealed in the brushwood, had been watching the bridal procession, and now came to the rescue of his true love. When the old lord heard of this he came to his senses and gave the lovers his blessing. Some weeks later a bridal procession advanced from the Clement's Chapel up to the festively decorated Castle Rheinstein. Trumpets were blown and horns resounded. Much more joyfully than on the previous occasion the musicians marched in front. Upon a milkwhite palfrey, as formerly, sat a noble maiden in bridal state, clothed in undulating robes bordered with fur. Her head was bent in maiden modesty as she listened to the endearments which the youthful knight whispered in her ear. Behind rode the father of the bride sunk in thought, and along with him was his pious sister Notburge, the canoness of Nonnenwerth.

A life of unalloyed married bliss followed this union, and God granted to the noble pair a long and happy life. They rest together in front of the altar in the Clement's Chapel which is situated across the Rhine from Assmannshausen. Burg Rheinstein has renewed its youth, and still from its precipitous height proudly overlooks the waters of our noble stream.

Castle Sooneck

The Blind Archer

*

In his stronghold at Sooneck, Siebold, one of the most rapacious of the robber barons presided over a godless revel. Wanton women with showy apparel and painted cheeks lolled in the arms of tipsy cavaliers. The music blared, and to complete their carousal wine flowed freely. The lord of Sooneck flushed with drinking, and leering on the assembly with evil-looking eyes spoke as follows:

"Noble ladies (drunken applause from his worthy associates) and much-married nobles (loudly giggled the shameless females), after food and drink, I, as your host will be pleased to entertain you by bringing before you a ferocious animal which I keep confined here."

While the ladies pretended to take shelter timidly behind their lords, and the men stared at their host expecting some further explanation, the doors of the room opened, and led by two servants a man in coarse garments, and with unkempt hair and beard stood before them. A suppressed whisper passed round the festive board and all eyes were fixed on the haggard countenance of the prisoner. When for a moment the weary eyelids were raised, two ghastly cavities were visible. Again, with the same tone of levity, the lord of the castle spoke, "Lovely ladies, and knightly companions, the best marksman on the Rhine was Hans Veit of Fürsteneck. Like ourselves he was dreaded far and near. He and I entered on a feud of life and death. He went down."

„With broken and battered shield, bleeding from numerous wounds I lay prostrate before you awaiting manfully the death-thrust," murmured the prisoner, and his voice sounded as if from the grave. "It pained me to finish him off," said

Siebold flippantly, "I got his two eyes taken out, and thus added to my collection of rarities, the best archer on the Rhine."

"My murdered eyes behold your scorn," said the prisoner harshly. "But surely chivalry still flourishes on Sooneck" said the lord of the castle. "Understand then that my servants have informed me, that even blind, you can, guided only by sounds, hit a given mark with a bolt. If you come out of this ordeal successful, freedom shall be the reward." Stormy applause greeted these words.

"Death were dearer to me than life," murmured the blind archer. As he seized the crossbow however, a gleam of joy went over his countenance like a ray of sunshine over a sombre landscape. Crowded together in a corner of the room the guests watched the proceedings. The lord of Sooneck seized a goblet and ordered the prisoner to draw upon it, after hearing the sound. In the next moment the silver clang resounded, as the goblet fell on the floor.

"Shoot now," said Siebold of Sooneck, and immediately an arrow pierced his mouth. With a grunt like a slaughtered ox, Siebold sank among the rushes. Silent and motionless with the two eye-cavities gaping, stood the blind man. Then his shaggy head sank on his heaving breast. Like a flock of frightened crows the knights and their paramours fled, and only a few terrified squires and servants muttered prayers over the body of the lord of Sooneck.

Kaub

Castle Gutenfels

*

About the middle of the thirteenth century, there was a stately castle near Kaub which was inhabited by Count Philip of Falkenstein. There he lived very happily with his beautiful sister Guta, who was as good as she was fair.

At the coffin of emperor Heinrich IV.

Numerous knights had sought to win her love, but none had achieved this conquest, the castle maiden having no desire to exchange her brother's hospitable home for any other.

At that time a magnificent tournament was held at Cologne, to which knights from all countries of the kingdom far and near and even from England were invited.

A great multitude of spectators were assembled to see the stately knights contending for the prize, which a fair hand would bestow on them.

Among the nobles present at the tournament was a knight from England, whose graceful figure and splendid armour were particulary striking. He wore a veiled visor, and the stewards of the tournament announced him under the name of "the Lion Knight," a golden lion ornamenting his shield. Soon the majestic knight's master-like manner of fighting created a great sensation, and when he succeeded in unhorsing his opponent, a most formidable combatant, loud rejoicings rang through the lists.

Count Philip and his sister were among the guests. Guta had been watching the strange knight with ever increasing interest during the tournament, regretting at the same time that she could not see his face.

But an opportunity soon presented itself when the knight was declared victor. She was selected to present the prize, a golden laurel-wreath, to the winner, she became much embarrassed, and a feeling such as she had never before experienced seized her as she looked at the Briton's face for the first time.

Perhaps the knight may have read in the lovely maiden's countenance what she in vain tried to hide from him, perhaps a spark from that passionate fire which had so suddenly fired her heart, may have flown into his soul as he knelt before her to receive the wreath, which she placed on his head with a trembling hand. Who can tell?

Afterwards when these two were conversing together in subdued whispers, the knight silently admiring her grace and the maiden scarcely able to restrain her feelings, the thoughts which he longed to tell her, flamed in his heart. The same evening in the banqueting hall, when the music was sounding within its walls, he was Guta's inseparable companion, and eloquent words flowed from his lips telling her of the love which his eyes betrayed.

The proud stranger begged Guta for her love and swore to be hers; he told her he must at once return to his country where urgent duty called him, but that he would come back to claim her in three months' time. Then he would publicly sue for her hand and declare his name, which circumstances compelled him to keep secret for the time being.

Love will make any sacrifice; Guta accepted her lover's pledge willingly, and thus they parted under the assurance that they would soon meet again.

Five months had passed. That terrible

time ensued when Germany became the battlefield of the party-struggles over the election of the emperor. Conrad IV. the last of the house of Hohenstaufen, had died in Italy. In the northern countries there was a great rising against William of Holland who was struggling for the imperial throne; Alphonso of Castile was chosen king in one part of the country, while Richard of Cornwall, son of John, king of England, was elected in another; but Richard, having received most influential votes, was crowned at Aix-la-Chapelle, and from thence he started on a journey through the Rhine provinces, to the favour of which he had been chiefly indebted for his election.

Spring was casting her bright beams over waves and mountains in the valley of the Rhine, but in Falkenstein castle no ray of sunshine penetrated the gloom. Guta, pale and unhappy, sat within its walls, weaving dreams which seemed destined never to be fulfilled. Sometimes she saw her lover dying on a terrible battle field with her name on his lips, then again laughing and bright with a maiden from that far-off island in his arms, talking derisively of his sweetheart on the Rhine. She became more and more conscious that she had given him her first love, and that he had cruelly deceived her. Sorrow and grief had taken possession of her, and all her brother's efforts to amuse her and to distract her attention were in vain.

A great sound of trumpets was heard one day on the highway, and a troop of knights stopped at the castle. Guta saw the train of warriors from her window, where she had been sitting weeping. The count w. chivalrous hospitality received them, and led them into the banqueting-hall. His astonishment was great, when he recognised the bold Briton, the victor at the tournament in Cologne, as leader of this brilliant retinue, he who had broken his secret pledge to his beloved sister. A dark glance took the place of the friendly expression on his face. The Briton seemed to notice it and pressing Philip's hand said cordially, "I am Richard of Cornwall, elected Emperor of Germany, and I have come here to solicit the hand of your sister Guta, who promised herself to me five months ago in Cologne. I come late to redeem my promise, but my love is unchanged. I beg you to announce my arrival to her without betraying my name."

Philip bowed deeply before the illustrious guest, and the retainers respectfully retired to a distance. The great guest strode up and down the room impatiently. Then the doors were suddenly thrown open, and a beautiful figure appeared on the threshold, her face glowing with emotion.

With a low cry Guta threw herself into her lover's arms, and the first moments of their reunion were passed in silent happiness.

Philip now entered the room unperceived, and revealed the secret to his sister. The maiden in great confusion and shame stole a look at her lover's eyes, and he, drawing her gently to him, asked her to share all — even his throne with him.

Shortly afterwards Richard celebrated his marriage with imperial magnificence at the castle on the Rhine, which Philip thence forward called Gutenfels, in honour of his sister.

Castle Lahneck

The Templars of Lahneck

*

On the opposite side of the Rhine from Coblenz, and towering above Lahnstein, rises Castle Lahneck, a keep shaped somewhat in the form of a pentagon. Lahneck succumbed to the hordes of Louis XIII. in the same year as the castle of Heidelberg was destroyed. The following stirring tale is associated with Lahneck.

It was the Templars of Jerusalem who erected this fortress whose imposing watch-tower rises nearly 100 feet above the main building. The riches of the Templars led to their destruction. The contemptible French king, Philip the Fair, by making grave complaints to the Pope obtained an order for the abolition of this much-abused order, and dragged the Grand Master with fifty of his faithful followers to the stake. Everywhere a cruel policy of extermination was immediately adopted against the outlawed knights, the chief motive of the persecutors being rather a desire to confiscate the rich possessions of the Templars than any religious zeal against heretics and sinners.

Peter von Aspelt, Archbishop of Mainz, had cast envious eyes on proud Lahneck which sheltered twelve Knights-Templars and their retainers. Alleging some faulty conduct on the part of the soldiers of the cross, he gave orders that the castle should be razed, and that the knights should exchange the white mantle with the red cross for the monk's cowl, but to this the twelve as knights sans peur et sans reproche issued a stout defiance. This excited the greed and rage of the archbishop all the more. From the pontiff, whom with his own hands he had successfully nursed on his sick-bed at Avignon, Peter von Aspelt procured full power over the goods and lives of the excommunicated knights of Lahneck. He then proceeded down the Rhine with many vassals and mercenaries, and presented the Pope's letter to the Templars, at the same time commanding them to yield. Otherwise their castle would be taken by storm, and the inmates as impenitent sinners would die a shameful death on the gallows. The oldest of the twelve, a man with silvery hair, advanced and declared in the name of his brethren, that they were resolved to fight to the last drop of their blood, and further, that they were quite prepared to suffer like their brethren in France. And so the fight between such fearful odds began. Many

soldiers of the Electorate fell under
the swords of the knights and their faithful servants, but ever the furious archbishop ordered forward new bands to fill
the gaps. Day by day the ranks of the
defenders became thinner. Prominent
everywhere in this hand to hand struggle
where the heroic forms of the twelve
Templars, in white mantle with blood-red
cross. At last, at a breach which had been
defended with leonine courage, one of
the noble twelve sank beneath his shattered
shield, and closed his eyes in death.
A second shared his fate, then a third.
The others, bleeding from many wounds
and aided by the sorely diminished rem-
nant of their retainers, redoubled their
brave efforts, but still death made havoc
in their ranks. When, on the evening
of the day of fiercest onslaught the victorious besiegers planted their banner on
the captured battlement, the silver-haired
veteran, the former spokesman, stood with
blood-flecked sword among the bodies
of his fallen comrades, the last survivor.

Touched by such noble heroism the arch-bishop informed him that he would be allowed to surrender; but calling down the curse of heaven on worldly churchmen and their greed of land, he raised on high his sword and rushed upon his foes. Pierced with many wounds the last of the twelve sank to the earth, and over the corpse of this noble man the soldiers of Mainz pressed into the fortress itself.

Peter von Aspelt preserved Lahneck as a place of defence and residence for an officer of the Electorate of Mainz, and nominated as first holder of the post, Hartwin von Winningen. The castle remained in the possession of the Electorate of Mainz for 300 years, but the sad story of the twelve heroic Templars is remembered in the neighbourhood of Lahneck to this day.

Rolandseck

Knight Roland

*

The Emperor Charlemagne was surrounded by a circle of proud knights, the flower of whom was Count Roland of Angers, nephew of the King of the Franks. The name of no knight was so famous in battle and in tournaments as his. Helpless innocency adored him, his friends admired, and his enemies esteemed him. His chivalrous spirit had no love for the luxuries of life, and scorning to remain inactive at the emperor's court, he went to his imperial uncle, begging leave to go and travel in those countries of the mighty kingdom of the Franks, which up to that time were unknown to him. In his youthful fervour he longed for adventures and dangers. The emperor was much grieved to part with the brave knight, but however, he willingly complied with his request.

One day early in the morning the gallant hero left his uncle's palace near the Seine, rode towards the Vosges Mountains, accompanied by his faithful squire. The first object of his journey was castle Niedeck near Haslach, and from there he visited Attic, Duke of Alsace.

He continued his travels, and one evening as he was riding through the mountains, the glittering waters of the Rhine, washing both sides of the plain, greeted him. The river in that part of the country offered him few charms in its savage wildness, but he knew that the scenery would soon change. He moved on down the Rhine to where a gigantic mountain shuts the rushing current into a narrow space. Its foot stands chained in the floods, which only in places retire a little, thus leaving the poor folk a narrow stretch of land.

On the heights there were proud cas-

tles, telling the wanderer below of the
fame of their illustrious races. Thus Roland made many a long journey on his
adventurous course down the Rhine. He
passed many a place rich in old memories:
the Lorelei Rock, where the water nymph
sang at night: the cheerful little spot
where St. Goar lived and worked at the
time of Childebert, the Merovingian, (that
wonderful saint who once spread a fog
over his imperial uncle, compelling him
to pass the night in the open air, because
his Majesty, while journeying from Ingelheim to Coblenz had neglected to bend his
knee in his chapel) and the green mea-
dows near Andernach, where Genovefa,
wife of Palatine Count Siegfried lived.
And now Roland neared the place where
the stream reaches the end of the Rhine
Valley, and where the seven giants are
to be seen, the summit of one of which
is crowned with a castle; there they stand
like the seven knights who, in later times
stood weeping round the holy remains
of the German emperor.

A wooded island lay in the deep-blue waters. The setting sun threw a golden light over the hills. On the sides of the mountains there were numberless vineyards, to the left, hedges of beeches ascending to the heights of the rugged summits, to the right, the murmur of the rippling waters, and above, visible among the legendary rocks where once a terrible beast lived, the pinnacles of a knight's castle, and over all, the heavens clothed with a garment of silver stars.

The knight paused in silence; his glance rested admiringly on the beautiful picture. His steed pawed the ground uneasily with his bronze-shod hoofs, and his faithful squire looked anxiously at the darkening sky. He reminded his master modestly that it was time to seek shelter for the night.

"I should like to beg for it up there," said Roland dreamingly, an inexplicable feeling of sweet sadness coming over him for the first time. He bade his squire ask the boat-man who was putting out his little bark to cross the river, what was the name of the castle? The castle was the Drachenburg, where Count Heribert so-journed sometimes. Thus ran the answer which pleased Roland very much. He had been charged with many greetings and messages to the old count at the Drachen-burg from his friends living near the upper Rhine. Roland now hesitated no longer, and soon a boat was ploughing the dark waves.

II.

In the meantime night had come on. The full moon's soft beams showed them their way through the dark forest. Count Heribert, a worthy knight in the flower of his age, bade the nephew of his im-perial master heartily welcome to his castle. Far past midnight they stayed in the count's chambers, engaged in enter-taining conversation.

The next day Count Heribert presented his daughter Hildegunde to the knight. Roland's eyes, full of admiration, rested on the blushing young maiden. Never before had the charms of a woman awakened any deep feeling in his heart; he had only thirsted after glory and deeds of daring, after tournaments and feuds. Now the bold champion was struck with a shaft from the quiver of love. He who had opposed the dreaded adversary so often, now bowed his fearless head in almost girlish confusion before Hildegunde's charms. She, too, stood crimsoning deeply before the celebrated hero whose name was famous, and who was beloved in all the country round.

The old knight broke up the scene of embarrassing silence between the youthful couple with gay laughing words, and conducted his guest through the high halls of his castle.

Roland tarried longer at the friendly castle than he had ever done before in any other place in the country. He seemed bound to the blissful spot by love's indissoluble chains, and so it happened that one day these two found themselves,

Tournament in the middle ages

hand in hand, the deep love in their hearts rushing forth in ardent words. Count Heribert bestowed his lovely daughter very willingly on the celebrated knight, his only desire being to complete the happiness of his child whom he loved so dearly. A castle should be erected for her on the heights of the rocks on the other side of the Rhine, opposite the Drachenburg, and this proud fort on the rugged rocky corner of the mountain, should be a watch-tower for the glorious Seven Mountains and their castle. In later times it became the famous Rolandseck. Soon the walls could be seen raising themselves up, and every day the lovers stood on the balcony of the Drachenburg looking across, where industrious workmen and masons were busily toiling. Hildegunde began to weave sweet dreams of the future round her new home, where she meant to chain the adventurous hero with true love.

But one day a messenger appeared at the Drachenburg on a horse white with foam. He was sent by Charlemagne and brought the tidings of a crusade which the emperor had decreed against the Infidels beyond the Pyrenees. Charlemagne desired to have the famous knight among the leaders of his army. Roland received the message of his great master in silence. He looked at Hildegunde who with a death-like face was standing beside him. Grief stabbed cruelly at his heart, but he must obey the call of honour and duty, and, informing the royal messenger that he would arrive at the imperial camp in three days, he turned sorrowfully away, Hildegunde sobbing at his side.

III.

The cross and the half-moon were fighting furiously for the upper hand in Spain. Terrible battles were fought, and much blood flowed from both Christians and Infidels. Bloody victories were gained by the emperor's brave knights, the chief of whom was Roland. His sword forced a triumphant way for Charlemagne, it guarded his army, passing victoriously through the unknown country of the enemies. But the sad day of Ronceval, so often sung by German and other poets was yet to come. Separated from the main body of the army, Roland's brave rear-guard was making its way through the dusky forest. Suddenly wild shouts sounded from the heights, and the cowardly Moor pressed down on the little band, threatening them with destruction. But the noble Franks fought like lions. Roland's charger, Brilliador, flew now here, now there, and many a Saracen was hewn down by its noble rider's sword, Durand. But numbers conquer bravery. The little army of Franks became less and less, and at last Roland sank, struck by the lance of a gigantic Moor. The combat continued furiously round him. When night spread mournfully over the battle-field, the Infidels had already done their terrible work. The Franks lay dead; only a few had escaped from the slaughter.

"Where is Roland?" was the frightened cry from pale lips. He was not among the saved. "Where is Roland?" asked Charlemagne anxiously of the messengers. Through the whole kingdom their answers seemed to resound, Roland the hero had fallen in battle fighting against the Saracens; wherever this cry was heard, it awakened deep sorrow.

The news soon spread as far as the Rhine, and one day the imperial messengers appeared at the Drachenburg, bringing the sad tidings and the deepest sympathy of the emperor. Heribert sighed deeply on hearing the news and covered his eyes with his hands; Hildegunde's grief was heart-breaking. Before the altar of the Queen of sorrows she lay sobbing her heart out, imploring for comfort in her great need. For days on end she shut herself up in her little bower, and even her father's gentle sympathy could not assuage her bitter grief.

Weeks passed. Then one day the pale maiden entered the knight's chamber, her grief quite transfigured. He drew her softly towards him, and then she revealed the resolution which was in her heart. Count Heribert was overwhelmed with grief, but he pressed a loving kiss on her pure forehead.

The day came, when down below on the island Nonnenwert, the convent bells rang solemnly. A new novice, Count Heribert's lovely daughter, knelt before the altar. In the holy stillness of the convent she sought the peace which she could not find in the castle of her father. With a last great convulsive sob she had torn her lover's name from her heart, had quenched the flame of sorrowing love for him, and now her soul was to be filled ever with the holy fire of the love of God. In vain her afflicted father hoped that the unaccustomed loneliness of the convent would shake her resolution, and that when the first year's trial was over, she would return to him. But no! the pious young maiden fervently begged the bishop, who was a relation of her father,

to release her from the year's trial
and to allow her after a short time to take
her final vows. Her longing desire was
fulfilled. After a month Hildegunde's golden locks were no more, and the lovely
daughter of the Drachenburg was dedicated to the Lord forever.

IV.

Time rolled on. Spring had vanished
and the sheaves were ripening in the
fields. Where the river reaches the end
of the Rhine valley crowned by the Seven
Giants, a knight with his horse stopped
to rest. Far away in the south, where the
valley of Ronceval lies bathed in sunshine,
he had lain in the hut of a poor herd.
There the faithful squire had dragged his
master pierced by a Moorish lance. The
bold hero and leader had remained for
weeks and months on his sick-bed struggling with death, till the force of his iron
nature had at last conquered. Roland was
recovering under loving care, while they

were mourning him as dead in the land of the Franks. Then having recovered, he hurried back to the Rhine urged by an irresistible longing.

A wooded island lay in the deep-blue waters. The setting sun threw a golden light over the hills; numberless vineyards flanked the mountains, hedges of beeches were on one side, the murmur of waters on the other, and above the pinnacles of a knight's castle among the legendary rocks where once a terrible beast lived, over all the heavens clothed with a garment of silver stars.

Silently the knight paused, his glance resting admiringly on the beautiful picture. Now as in months before an inexplicable feeling of sweet sadness came over the dreamer.

"Hildegunde!" murmured Roland, glancing up at the starry heavens. Again as formerly a boat-man rowed across the stream, and Roland soon was striding through the forest towards the Drachenburg, accompanied by his faithful squire.

The old watchman at the castle stared at the late guest, and crossing himself, he rushed up to the chambers of his master. A man's figure, bent with age and sorrow, tottered forward. "Roland!" he gasped forth. The knight supported the broken-down old man in his arms. When Roland had departed long ago, his grief had found no tears; now they flowed abundantly down his cheeks.

The knight tore himself from the other's arms. "Where is she?" he asked in a hoarse voice, "dead?" Count Heribert looked at him with unspeakable sorrow. "Hildegunde, bride of Roland whom they supposed dead, is now a bride of Heaven."

The hero groaned aloud, covering his face with his hands.

In spring he left the Drachenburg and went to the castle on the rocky corner, and there he laid down his arms for ever; his thirst for action was quenched. Day by day he sat over there, looking silently down on the green island in the Rhine, where the nun, Hildegunde, wandered about among the flowers in the convent garden every morning. Sometimes indeed it seemed that she bowed kindly to him, then the knight's face would be lighted up with a gleam of his old happiness.

But even this joy was taken from him. One day his beloved did not appear; and soon the death-bell tolled sorrowfully over the island. He saw a coffin which they were carrying to its last resting-place, and he heard the nuns chanting the service for the dead, he saw them all, only one was wanting ... then he covered his face. He knew whom they were carrying to the grave.

Autumn came, withering the fresh green on Hildegunde's tomb. But Roland still kept his watch, gazing motionlessly at the little churchyard, and one day his squire found him there, cold and dead, his half-closed eyes turned towards the place where his loved one was sleeping.

For many a century the proud castle which they called Rolandseck, crowned the mountain. Then it fell into ruins, like the mighty Drachenburg, the tower of which is still standing. Fifty years ago the last arches of Roland's castle were blown down one stormy night, but later on they were built up again in memory of this tale of true and faithful love in the olden times.

The Drachenfels

*

When the wanderer has left the "city of the Muses," Bonn, he perceives to the left the mighty summits of the Seven Mountains. The rocky point of one of these hills is still crowned by the tower and walls of an old knight's castle. A most touching legend is related of the mountain with the terrible name.

In the first centuries after the birth of the world's Redeemer, the Germans on the left side of the Rhine accepted willingly the doctrines of the Cross; Maternus, a disciple of the great Apostle, had brought them over from Gaul. At first the pious messenger of Christ worked among the heathen tribes in vain. They persisted in their paganism, and even prevented the priests from coming into their country.

At that time there was a terrible dragon living in the hollow of the rock which even now is called the Dragon's hole. He was of a hideous form, and every day he used to leave his den and rage through the forests and valleys, threatening men and animals. Human strength was powerless against this monster; the people thought that an angry deity had his abode in this terrible beast, so they bestowed godlike honours on him, sacrificing criminals and prisoners to him.

A tribe of heathens lived at the foot of the mountain. These men, desirous of war, often made raids on the neighbouring countries, carrying fire and sword among their Christian brothers. They once crossed the water, plundering the land and making prisoners of the people. Among the latter there was one most lovely maiden, whose beauty and grace inflamed two of the leaders so much, that each of them desired to have her for himself. One was called Horsrik the Elder, a famous chieftain, known to have the strength of a bear and the wildness of a tiger; the other, Rinbold, of a less rough nature, but of equal bravery.

The beautiful maiden turned aside shuddering when she saw the two chief's glaring eyes, contending for possession of her. All round were their men intoxicated with victory. The struggle for the Christian maid affected the two leaders more than the division of the booty. Soon the angry words of the two opponents found an echo in the hearts of the men standing round.

Horsrik, the much-feared fighter, claimed her, and was received with cheers. Rinbold, the proud young chieftain, claimed her also, — great applause greeted him. The former glared sternly, grasping his club in a threatening manner. The high-priest, an old man with silver-white hair and stern features, stepped in between the two combatants, and in a voice surging with anger he said:

"Cursed be every dissension for the possession of this stranger! A Christian must not disunite the noblest of our tribe. A daughter of those we hate, she shall fall to nobody's share. She, the author of so much strife, shall be sacrificed to the Dragon, and shall be dedicated to Woden's honour at the next rising of the sun."

The men murmured applause, Horsrik more than the rest. The maiden held her head upright. Rinbold, the proud young chieftain, looked sorrowfully at her angel-like face.

II.

Early the following day before the sun had poured his bright beams on the earth, the valley showed signs of life. Through the dusk of the forest a noisy procession moved upwards towards the highest point, the priest in the middle, behind him the prisoner, pale but resolute.

Silently, for her Lord's sake, she had
allowed the priest to bind her forehead
as a victim, and to place consecrated flowers in her loose flowing hair. Many a
sympathetic look from the crowd had
been cast at the steadfast maiden. The
young chieftain was stricken with pain
at the sight of her death-like countenance.

There stood the projecting rock which
had often been dishonoured by human
blood. The fanatical priests wound ropes
round the maiden's body, and then tied
her to St. Woden's tree which overhung
the precipice. No complaint escaped the
Christian's white lips, no tears glistened
in her eyes which were glancing up at
the morning sky. The throng of people
moved off, waiting silently in the distance
to see what would happen.

The first rays of the sun streamed over
the mountain; they lighted up the wreath
of flowers in the maiden's hair, playing
about her lovely face, and crowning it
with glory. The Christian maid was await-

ing death, as a bride awaits her bride-groom, her lips moving slightly as in prayer.

A gloomy sound came up from the depths. The Dragon started from his den, spitting fire on his path. He cast a look at his victim there on the spot which his blood-thirsty maw knew so well. He raised his scaly body, thus letting his sharp claws be more visible, moved his snaky tail in a circle, and showed his gaping mouth. Snorting the monster crawled along, shooting flames out of his bloodshot eyes.

A shudder of death crept over the maiden at the sight of this awful beast. Tremblingly she tore a sparkling golden crucifix from her breast, held it towards the monster piteously, and called on her Lord in a heart-rending voice. Wonder of wonders! Raising himself, as if struck by lightning, the monster turned, dashing himself backwards over the jagged stones into the waters below, and disappearing in the river among the falling rocks.

Wondering cries arose from the waiting heathens. Astonishment and wonder were depicted on every face. In quiet submission, her eyes half-closed, the maiden stood, praying to Him who had saved her. The cords fell from her sides; two strong arms caught her and carried her into the midst of the astonished crowd. She raised her eyes and perceived the younger of the two chieftains. His rough warlike hand had seized hers. The young man bent his knees as if to a heavenly being, and touched her white fingers with his lips, Loud applause greeted him on all sides.

The old priest came forward, the people waiting in great expectation. "Who had saved her from certain destruction? Who was the God who so visibly aided His own?" asked he solemnly of the Christian. With bright eyes the maiden answered triumphantly:

"This picture of Christ has crushed the Dragon and saved me. The salvation of the world and the welfare of man lies in

Him." The priest glanced at the crucifix with reverent awe.

"May it soon lighten your spirit and those of all these people round," said the maiden earnestly. "It will reveal greater wonders than this to you, for our God is great."

The maiden and all the other prisoners were conducted back to their own country. But the former soon returned again, accompanied by a Christian priest. The voice of truth and innocence worked wonders in the hearts of the heathens. Thousands were converted and baptized. The old priest and Rinbold were the first who bowed their heads in submission to the new doctrine. Great rejoicings were held among the tribe when the maiden gave her hand to the young chieftain. A Christian temple was erected in the valley, and a splendid castle was built on the summit of the rocks for the newly-married couple. For about ten centuries their descendants flourished there, a very powerful race in the Rhine countries.

The Monk of Heisterbach

*

In olden times in a lovely valley near the Seven Mountains, stood a cloister called Heisterbach. Even now parts of the walls of this old monastery remain, and it was not by the hand of time, but by the barbarism of foolish warfare, that its halls fell into ruins. The monks were driven away, the abbey was pulled down, and the stones were used for the building of a fortress.

Since that time, so the country folk relate, the spirits of the banished monks wander nightly among the ruins, raising mute accusations against their persecutors and the destroyers of their cells. Among them there was one, Gebhard, the last Prior of Heisterbach, who now, they say, wanders about the graves of the monks, and also haunts the burial-places of the Masters of Löwenburg and Drachenburg.

In the Middle Ages the monks of Heisterbach were very famous. Many a rare copy of the Holy Scriptures, many highly learned piece of writing was sent out into the world from this hermitage, telling of the industry and learning of the pious monks.

There was one brother, still young in years, who distinguished himself by his learning. He was looked up to by all the other brethren, and even the gray-haired Father Prior had recourse to his stores of knowledge. But the poisonous worm of doubt began to gnaw at his soul; the mirror of his faith was blurred by his deep meditations. His keen eye would often wander over the faded parchment on which the living word of God was written, while his childlike believing heart, humbly submitting itself, would lamentingly cry out, "Lord, I believe, help Thou mine unbelief!" Like a ghost his restless doubts would hover about him, making his soul the scene of tormenting struggle.

One night with flushed face he had been meditating over a parchment. At daybreak he still remained engrossed in his thoughts. The morning sun threw his bright rays over the heavens, casting playful beams on the written roll in the monk's hands.

But he saw them not, his thoughts were wholly taken up by a passage which for months past had ever been hidden to him and had been the constant subject of his reflections, "A thousand years are but as a day in Thy sight."

His brain had already long tormented itself over the obscure words of the Psalmist, and with a great effort he had striven to blot it out of his memory, and now the words danced again before his weary eyes, growing larger and larger. Those confusing black signs seemed to become a sneering doubt hovering round him: "A thousand years are but as a day in Thy sight."

He tore himself away from the silent cell, seeking the cool solitude of the cloister-gardens. There with a heavy heart he paced the paths, torturing himself with horrid doubts.

His eyes were fixed on the ground, his mind was far away from the peaceful garden, and without being aware of what he was doing, he left the cloister gardens and wandered out into the neighbouring forest. The birds in the trees greeted him cordially, the flowers opened their eyes at his approach; but the wretched man heard and saw nothing but the words: "A thousand years are but as a day in Thy sight."

His wandering steps grew feeble, his feverish brain weary from want of sleep. Then the monk sank down on a stone, and laid his troubled head against a tree.

A sweet, peaceful dream stole over his spirit. He found himself in spheres glowing with light; the waters of Eternity were rushing round the throne of the Most High; creation appeared and praised His works, and Heaven extolled their glory; from the worm in the dust, which no

Lohengrin, the swan's knight

earthly being has been able to create, to the eagle soaring above the heights of the earth: from the grain of sand on the sea-shore, to the gigantic crater, which, at the Lord's command, vomits fire out of its throat which has been closed for thousands of years: they all spoke with one voice which is not heard by the haughty, being only manifest and comprehensible to the humble. These were the words of Him who created them, be it in six days or in six thousand years, "A thousand years are but as a day in Thy sight."

With a slight shudder the monk opened his eyes.

"I believe Lord! help Thou my unbelief," murmured he, taking heart.

The bell sounded in the distance. They were ringing for vespers; sunset was already gleaming through the forest.

The monk hastily turned towards the cloister. The chapel was lighted up, and through the half-opened door he could see the brothers in their stalls. He hurried noiselessly to his place, but to his astonishment he found that another monk was there; he touched him lightly on the shoulder, and strange to tell, the man he saw was unknown to him. The brothers, now one, now another, raised their heads and looked in silent questioning at the new comer.

A peculiar feeling seized the poor monk, who saw only strange faces round him. Growing pale, he waited till the singing was over. Confused questions seemed to pass along the rows.

The Prior, a dignified old man with snowwhite hair, approached.

"What is your name, strange brother?" asked he in a gentle, kind tone. The monk was filled with dismay. "Maurus," murmured he in a trembling voice. "St. Bernhard was the Abbot who received my vows, in the sixth year of the reign of King Conrad, whom they called the Frank."

Incredulous astonishment was depicted on the brother's countenances.

The monk raised his face to the old

Prior and confessed to him how he had wandered out in the early morning into the cloister-gardens, how he had fallen asleep in the forest, and had not wakened till the bell for vespers sounded.

The Prior made a sign to one of the brothers. Then turning to the monk he said: "It is almost three hundred years since the death of St. Bernhard and of Conrad, whom they called the Frank."

The cloister annals were brought, and it was there found that three hundred years had passed since the days of St. Bernhard. The Prior also read the following note.

"A doubter disappeared one day from the cloister, and no one ever knew what became of him."

A shudder ran through the monk's limbs. This was he, this brother Maurus who had now come back to the cloister after three hundred years! What the Prior had read sounded in his ears as if it were the trumpet of the Last Judgment. Three hundred years!

With wide-open eyes he gazed before him, then stretched forth his hands as if seeking for help. The brothers supported him, observing him at the same time with secret dismay; his face had become ashy pale, like that of a dying person, the narrow circle of hair on his head had become snow-white.

"My brothers," murmured he in a dying voice, "value the imperishable word of the Lord at all times, and never try to fathom what he in His wisdom has veiled from us. May my example never be blotted out of your memory. Only to-day the words of the Psalmist were revealed to me. "A thousand years are but as a day in Thy sight. May he have mercy on me, a poor sinner." He sank lifeless to the ground, and the brothers, greatly moved, repeated the prayers for the dead over his body.

Cologne

Richmodis of Aducht

*

It was about the middle of the fifteenth century.

The shadows of death hovered above the holy City of Cologne. A strange figure in dark garments hurried with quick steps through the streets and lanes. It was the plague. Its poisonous breath penetrated into cottages and palaces, extinguishing the lives of many thousands.

The grave diggers marked innumerable houses with a black cross, to warn the passers-by that the destroying angel had entered there. The roll of the dead rose to such numbers that it was impossible to bury them all in the customary manner. Therefore the bodies of the unfortunate people were thrown together into a common grave, covered only scantily with earth and marked with a plain wooden cross.

Woe and sorrow thus filled the old City of Cologne.

On the New-market, close to the Church of the Apostles, in a splendid mansion, the rich Magistrate, Mengis of Aducht lived. Wealth could not save his house from the dreadful epidemic, his youthful and lovely wife, Richmodis, was seized with the plague and died. The grief of **her** lord was boundless. He passed the whole night by the remains of his beloved spouse, dressed her himself in the white wedding gown she had worn as a happy bride a few years before, decorated the coffin with sweet white flowers, and covered her with the precious jewels and costly rings she had loved so much. Then she was buried.

Night approached, and the clear starry sky looked peacefully down on the afflicted town.

Perfect stillness prevailed in God's acre.
— Suddenly a jarring sound like the opening of an old rusty lock was heard, and
two dark shadows glided among the graves,
on and on till they stopped before the
fresh mould which enclosed the body of
Richmodis of Aducht. — Those two knew
the spot, and well they might, for they
were the grave-diggers, and had prepared
this grave themselves on the previous day.

They were present when the lid of the
coffin was screwed down, and had with
hungry looks coveted the glittering precious stones Richmodis was to be buried
with.

Now they had come to rob the dead
body. With spade and shovel the wreaths
and flowers were quickly removed from
the mound, the earth dug up and the
coffin laid bare. In feverish haste, spurred
on by their greed, they burst the lid
open, and the dim light of their lantern
fell full on the mild pale face of the dead
woman. With haste the bolder of the two
wretches loosened the white waxen hands

folded together as in prayer, and tried to tear off the rings.

Suddenly the body quivered, and the white hands spread out. Aghast the robbers dropped their tools, scrambled in utmost terror out of the grave, and fled as if chased by the furies.

A painful long sigh rose from the depth of the grave, and after some time the white form of Richmodis who had been buried alive, emerged from the tomb.

With wide open eyes, full of horror, she looked down into the ghastly bed she had just left. — Could it really be true, or was it only a frightful dream?

God's acre was silent, but for the rustling of the autumn leaves of the weeping willows. Stillness of death everywhere! — No answer came to her faint cry for help — The horror of her situation however wakened her declining strength. She took up the lantern which the robbers had left behind them and with feeble steps reached the entrance of the churchyard.

The streets were desolate. The stars overhead alone perceived the slowly moving form, every now and then resting against the walls of the houses. — At last she reached the Newmarket and stood before the door of her home. Dark and quiet it seemed. But from the window in the magistrate's room a faint light shone forth. A quiver ran through the frame of the poor wife, and a wild longing desire seized her to be sheltered by his loving arms and to feel in his embrace that she had really returned to life again.

With a last effort she seized the knocker, and listened with newly awakened hope to the tapping sound which rang clear through the night.

A few minutes elapsed. Then an old servant peeping out of the window in the door, perceived the white ghostly figure of his late mistress. Horror seized him, his hair stood on end. Richmodis called him by his name and begged him to open the door. At the sound of her voice the old man started, ran upstairs, dashed into his master's room uttering incoherent sounds, and stammering: "O Lord, the dead rise; outside stands our good Mistress and demands entrance!" But the Magistrate shook his head in deep grief: "Richmodis, my beloved wife is dead and will never return, never, never," he repeated in unspeakable sorrow; "I will rather believe that my two white horses will burst from their halters in the stable and mount the stairs to the tower."

A terrible sound suddenly filled the quiet house, a noise like thunder was heard, and Mengis of Aducht and his servant saw the two white steeds tearing and tramping in haste upstairs.

A moment later two horses looked out of the tower windows into the night, and shortly afterwards the Magistrate laughing and crying with joy at the same time, held in his arms his wife who had returned from the grave.

For many years Richmodis lived happily with her husband, surrounded by several lovely children. Deep piety remained the motive power of Richmodis' being, and nobody ever saw her smile again.

If you come to Cologne, reader, you will still see the old house of the Aduchts at the Newmarket, with two white wooden horses' heads looking out of the top window.

The Goblins

*

This story goes back to the "good old times" of which we modern people always speak with a sigh of regret.

It was then when good-natured goblins appeared to mortal eyes, and tried to render the life of the troubled human race a little more cheerful. In groves and dens they had magnificent dwellings and watched there over the enormous mineral treasures of the earth.

Often these beneficent elves were busy miners or sometimes clever artisans. We all know that they manufactured the precious trinkets and arms of the Nibelungen treasure.

Deep in the interior of the earth they lived happily together, ruled over by a king. They could be called the harmless friends of darkness, because they were not allowed to come into broad daylight. If they did so, they were transformed into stones.

The goblins did not always remain underground. On the contrary they often came to the earth's surface through certain holes, called goblin-holes, but they always avoided meeting man.

Alas! the advance of civilisation has driven these friendly spirits gradually from the places where they used to do so much good. None of us, I am sure has ever had the good luck of meeting one of them.

The goblins were of different sizes. Sometimes they were as small as one's thumb, sometimes as large as the hand of a child of four years old. The most remarkable feature of these tiny figures was the enormous head and the pointed hump that so often adorned their backs. Their look was on the whole more comical than ugly. German people used to call them "Heinzchen" or "Heinzelmännchen."

A long time ago the good town of Cologne was inhabited by a host of dwarfs, and the honest population knew a great many stories about them. The workmen and artisans especially had, through the assistance of the little wights, far more holidays than are marked in the calendar.

When the carpenters for instance were lying on their benches in sweet repose, those little men came swiftly and stealthily along, they took up the tools and chiselled and sawed and hammered with a will, and thus, records the poetical chronicles which I am quoting, before the carpenters woke up, the house stood there finished.

In the same way things went on with the baker. While his lads were snoring, the little goblins came to help. They groaned under the load of heavy corn-sacks, they kneaded and weighed the flour, lifted and pushed the bread into the oven, and before the lazy bakers opened their eyes, the morning bread, brown and crisp, was lying in rows on the table.

The butchers too could speak of similar agreeable experiences. The good little men chopped, mixed and stirred with all their might, and when the drowsy butcher opened his eyes at last, he found the fresh, steaming sausages adorning the walls of his shop.

The cooper enjoyed also the help of the busy dwarfs, and even the tailor could not complain of the goblins having neglected him.

Once Mr. Cotton, a clever tailor, had the honour of making a Sunday coat for the mayor of the town. He worked diligently at it, but you can easily imagine that in the heat of the summer afternoon, the needle soon dropped from his hand, and he fell fast asleep. Hush! — look there. One little goblin after the other crept cautiously from his hiding place.

They climbed on the table and began the tailor's work and stitched and sewed and fitted and pressed, as if they had been masters of the needle all their lives.

When Master Cotton awoke, he found to his great joy the mayor's Sunday coat ready made, and so neatly and well done that he could present the magnificent garment with pride to the head of the town.

The pretty wife of Mr. Cotton looked at this master-piece of her husband's art with a mischievous twinkle in her eyes.

In the night when her husband had fallen asleep, she rose from her bed without making the slightest noise, and scattered pease all over the floor of the workshop; she then put a half-finished suit on the table. She kept a small lantern hidden under her apron, and waited behind the door listening. Soon after the room was full of little men all tumbling, falling, and slipping over the pease. Yells and screams rose at the same time. The poor little men were indeed much bruised and hurt. Without stopping they ran downstairs and disappeared.

The tailor's wife heard the noise, and thought it good sport. When the yells were loudest, she suddenly opened the door to see her visitors, but she came too late. Not a single goblin was left behind.

Since that time the friendly dwarfs have never more been seen in Cologne, and in other places also they have entirely disappeared.

Jan and Griet

*

"There lived at Cologne on the old farm of Kümpchenshof a peasant who had a maid called Griet and a man-servant called Jan."

Thus begins the old well-known Rhenish song of "Jan van Werth," the celebrated general of the imperial cavalry at the time when the Swedes and French were taking advantage of the civil war in

Germany. But nobody except the inhabitants of the holy City of Cologne, knows that Jan van Werth was originally a simple labourer, and that he was indebted for his luck in life to his bad luck in love.

Jan was an industrious farmer boy with an upright character and a handsome face. Many a girl would not have rejected him as a sweetheart, but Jan's tender heart had long been captivated by the good looks of pretty Griet, the comely maid of the Kümpchenshof. His love could not long remain a secret. One day he confessed to her with sobs that he loved her dearly, and would with pleasure work and toil for her twice as much as he then did for his master. He spoke long and earnestly, and taking courage with every word he uttered, he at last put to her the all important question — would she become his wife?

Laughingly the pretty girl put her round arms akimbo, tossed her head back and looked at her honest suitor with a mocking twinkle in her eyes. Then she shook

Jan and Griet

her head energetically and said: "You are only a farmer's labourer, my dear boy, and will remain one most probably all your life. True, it is not your fault, but all the same I should prefer to marry a rich farmer with cows and oxen and horses."

Bitter anger rose in Jan's breast on hearing her talk so heartlessly, but he controlled himself. "Just as you like," he said sadly, and turned away from the haughty maid.

From that day he could not endure any longer the life at the farm, and pocketing his wages, he said good-bye for ever to the Kümpchenshof and became a soldier.

It was a furious war in which the German Emperor was engaged against the enemies of his country, and brave soldiers were rare. Any valiant warrior might distinguish himself and become an officer at that time.

The farmer-boy, Jan, soon won by his bravery and intrepidity the esteem of his superiors, and was promoted to the rank of colonel. Once when fighting against the Swedish troops he showed such determination and courage that he won the battle. After this brilliant act he was made a general. But the name of Jan van Werth became even more famous when he beat the French in a skirmish at Tüttlingen.

In another way also his good luck reconciled him to the first bitter disappointment caused by Griet's scornful answer. He married a lovely and noble young lady, who was very proud of becoming the wife of such a celebrated general.

Let us now look back and see what happened in the meantime to Griet. She had waited month after month and year after year for the rich farmer. But the longed-for suitor never made his appearance. Even in those by-gone days red cheeks and bright eyes were much less thought of than ducats and glittering gold.

As time went on Griet grew old, and though she would now have been content with a simple man for her sweetheart, not even such a one condescended to ask her to become his wife.

Little by little Griet gave up all hopes of ever marrying, and had to look out for a living to keep her in her old age from starving. Therefore she started a fruit stall at one of the large gateways of Cologne.

One day the good inhabitants of this town were in great excitement, and crowded in their best Sunday-clothes round the gate of St. Severin, where Griet sat at her apple-stall. They had come to meet Jan van Werth, the celebrated general, who was returning victorious at the head of his regiment.

There he was sitting on a powerful charger which was gorgeously covered with gilded trappings. On his fine head Jan wore a broad-brimmed hat with a flowing feather. Behind him rode his splendid soldiers. The body-guard of the town beat the drum enthusiastically, and the Cologne people called out: "Long live our Jan van Werth!"

When the celebrated general passed the gate, he stopped his horse just in front of Griet's apple baskets, and looking down upon the old wrinkled woman, met her questioning glance with an odd smile. "Ah Griet," said he slowly, "whoever would have thought it?" At the sound of his voice an expression of sudden recognition passed over her worn features, and she muttered sorrowfully, but still audibly to the proud rider, "Oh, Jan, if I had only known it!"

A magnificent monument in the form of the statue of Jan van Werth now stands in the centre of the old market of Cologne.

It was erected there in memory not only of the heroic deeds of the brave general, but also as a warning to all Cologne maidens not to reject their suitors because they are poor, for one day, like Jan van Werth, they may become famous, and then they will not, like Griet, have to sigh over things that "might have been."

Cleves
Lohengrin

*

The weathercock on the ancient strong-hold at Cleves is a swan, and in olden times the dynasty that ruled over the lovely country round Cleves had also a swan in their crest. A legend, tragic and beautiful, preserved to posterity forever in Richard Wagner's lovely opera, is connected with it, — the legend of Lohengrin.

Long centuries ago deep sorrow brooded over the walls of the castle at Cleves. Its mistress, the Duchess Elsa was in great distress. Her beloved husband had died, and his remains had been brought to their last resting-place. As soon as the tomb had closed over them, one of the late Duke's vassals, Telramund, rose in revolt, and imperiously claimed the right to reign over the dukedom. The audacious man the whole plain. But none of the bright warriors came forward to take up the combat for Elsa's sake.

On the contrary deep silence followed the third challenge, and everybody's eyes were fixed on the forsaken princess who looked in her abandoned position still more lovely. The little hope that had till that moment given her strength to bear her misfortune, had now entirely vanished. In her utter desolation she offered a fervent prayer to heaven. On her rosary, so the legend records, a little silver bell was hanging, which possessed the wonderful gift of giving forth, whenever slightly touched, a clear ringing sound audible even at a great distance. In praying to God for deliverance from her great trouble, she pressed the cross on her rosary fervently to her lips. The silver bell tinkled, and at the same moment a little barge suddenly appeared on the blue river. When it came nearer, everybody looked with astonishment at the strange vessel. Its form was light and graceful; but what astonished the people most was that it was not moved by either oar or rudder, but was gently gliding on the blue waves drawn by a snow-white swan. In the middle of the vessel stood a knight in shining silver armour.

Long golden locks emerged from under his glittering helmet, his bright blue eyes looked boldly over the crowd on the shore, and his hand held the hilt of his broadsword firmly.

The strange boat stopped just opposite the plain where the people stood motionless with amazement. The knight landed from the barge, giving a sign with his hand to the swan, which swam gently down the Rhine.

In silence and awe the multitude made room for the stranger who approached with firm steps towards the middle of the brilliant circle, and saluted the assembly with a solemn grace. Then he bent his knees before the Duchess and rising, turned towards Telramund, challenging him proudly to fight with him for the hand and dominion of Elsa of Brabant. The bold rebel's temerity seemed to fail him for a few moments, but gathering fresh courage he pulled his sword from its sheath with a loud scornful laugh.

The next moment the two knights darted at each other, their blades clashing in rapid strokes.

The whole crowd looked with wonder and amazement at the strange knight's great prowess. He parried the blows of his strong adversary skilfully. The combat lasted for some time, and neither of the fighters seemed to give way. Suddenly a subdued cry was heard, and at the same time the presumptuous vassal sank to the ground, pierced by the sword of him whom God had sent, and expired. A tremendous shout of joy burst from the gazing crowd, which rang from one end of the plain to the other and was echoed by the glittering waves of the Rhine. The people rejoiced in the victory, and thought that God himself had decided the combat in favour of Elsa.

The Duchess felt greatly moved. In her overflowing gratitude she sank down before her deliverer with tears in her eyes. But he bade her rise, and bowing low before her asked her to become his wife. She consented. What a heaven of bliss opened for the Duchess of Brabant! All her former troubles were forgotten.

Her gratitude towards her rescuer was transformed into passionate love, to which Lohengrin, the virtuous knight, resdonded with tender adoration.

Yet though everything seemed now so serene in the life of the Duchess, there was a dim cloud which threatened to darken the clear prospect of her happiness. On their wedding-day Elsa had to promise her bridegroom that she would never inquire about his name, his home, or his descent.

Trusting her deliverer's honour and chivalrous bearing, she took the strange oath without a moment's hesitation.

Many years of bliss and happiness passed, and Elsa of Brabant had strictly kept the promise she had made on her bridal morning. Their happiness was still more enhanced by the birth of three hopeful boys. They were their parents' joy, and promised to become in future shining ornaments of knighthood.

It happened however, when the eyes of the Duchess were resting with pride on her sons, that her mother's heart thought with grief of the solemn oath she had sworn on her wedding-day.

With how much more pride would she have looked upon her sons if she could have known them to be the offspring of a high and noble race. She did not doubt however that her beloved husband's lineage was a most noble one. Yet the thought that his sons might never bear their father's name, nor be able to add new glories to it, was lying heavily on her mind, and darkened the radiant image of her husband, that like a deity filled her whole soul.

The fatal question she had for so long

withheld burst one day forcibly from her lips.

When she had pronounced the awful words, the proud hero grew pale, and freeing himself softly from her tender embrace, he cried out in bitter grief: "Woe to thee, my beloved wife and woe also to me! Now that thou hast uttered the question thou didst swear solemnly never to ask, our happiness is gone for ever. I must part from thee, never to see thee again."

A cry of anguish rose from her lips, but she was unable to keep him back. Waving his hand to her in a mute farewell her noble husband left the castle. He went to the Rhine and blew his silver horn.

Its sound was echoed from the shore like a long sob. The white swan with the boat soon appeared gliding gently over the river.

Lohengrin stepped into the boat and soon vanished out of sight and was seen no more.

His unhappy wife was inconsolable. Her grief was so intense that a short time after her health gave way, and she sank into a premature grave.

Her sons became the ancestors of a noble and distinguished race in the Rhenish country. Their badge is a swan.

The traveller who visits Cleves will still find a tombstone in its church with a knight carved on it, and a swan sitting at his feet.

Xanten
Siegfried

*

Siegfried, — and as we pronounce this glorious name, the hero looks forth at us with shining eyes, for was not Siegfried the perfect embodiment of all that was beautiful and good?

For centuries stories have been told and poems have been sung of the bold adventures of the young hero, whose energy only found satisfaction in victorious fights.

The original name of the small town on the lower Rhine now called Xanten, was "Ad Santos," "peace for the saints." It was thus named on account of the pious warriors of the Theban legion who in the fourth century had boldly died there for their creed under their leader, Victor.

At the time to which our story refers, a mighty stronghold formed the centre of the little town Xanten. A king called Siegmund with his wife Siegelinde and their son Siegfried lived there.

While a mere boy, Siegfried had already a kingly stature, and an almost untamable disposition of mind. When he was only thirteen years of age, his longing for grand deeds was so great that he found it impossible to remain inactive at home. From old songs and legends which the minstrels recited in his father's castle, he had heard so much of bold adventures and brilliant exploits performed by his forefathers, that he was most anxious to follow in their steps. He felt strong and valiant enough to undertake like the heroes of old, dangerous journeys. Therefore young Siegfried left one day his ancestral halls, and wandered southwards along the clear blue river. He soon found an opportunity of testing his courage.

At the foot of the Seven Mountains lived a celebrated armourer called Mimer, renowned for making excellent swords. Our hero liked this warlike trade, and he asked the master to receive him as an apprentice, that he might learn the praise-worthy art of forging a good sword for himself. The armourer agreed, and Siegfried remained at Mimer's workshop. The journeymen with whom the youth had to work, soon learned the enormous strength of their new companion. The boy, often not knowing how to give expression to his desire for action, would take up his fellow-workmen, lift them high into the air, and drop them, not always softly to the ground. Or when his anger was roused, he would imprint black and blue marks on their backs with his strong fists. Once he even smashed with one stroke of his hammer all the iron bars in the armoury, and knocked the anvil into the ground with a mighty blow.

Mimer looked on with dismay, amazed at the boy's almost supernatural strength, but fearing that Siegfried's wrath might some time turn against him, he thought to rid himself of his dangerous apprentice, and conceived a cunning plan to kill him. A horrible dragon lived in the neigbouring forest, which tore every wanderer to pieces who chanced to cross its way. Mimer ordered Siegfried to fetch a sack from the charcoal-burner in that forest, well knowing that the boy would never return thence.

The youth, without knowing the danger he was about to meet, went cheerfully on his way. In the middle of the thick wood he kindled a charcoal-kiln, and amused himself by putting big burning branches and young trees into the fire.

Suddenly the monster came swiftly

creeping on its huge claws. Curving its shimmering body the ugly beast opened wide its jaws to devour the young charcoal-burner. Siegfried's eyes brightened up at the prospect of an encounter with the terrible animal before him. Without a moment's hesitation, he tore a flaming beam out of the kiln, and pushed its burning end deep into the open mouth of the dragon. Roaring with pain the monster turned round beating violently with its prickly tail, trying in its agony to crush Siegfried. But he, jumping skilfully aside, rapidly dealt it heavy blows, and succeeded at last in smashing its head with a large piece of rock. He severed the head from the body, and threw it into the blazing flames. To his astonishment he observed how a stream of grease gushed from the burning pile, and collected in a pool at his feet.

Close by the charcoal-kiln stood an old lime-tree. A little bird sang merrily in its branches. Siegfried, involuntarily listening to the clear strain, made out the following words: "If you would be covered with horn, and become invulnerable, undress yourself and plunge into the pool."

Siegfried quickly threw his clothes off and anointed his whole body with the dragon's grease. While thus occupied a leaf from the old lime-tree above dropped between his shoulders. This part of the hero's body remained without horn. When he had finished, he took up the monster's head and returned to Mimer's workshop. The nearer he got to the smithy, the more his rage against his wicked master increased. Mimer had seen the boy from afar approaching with the trophy of his fight, and had hidden in great fear.

Siegfried however soon found him out and slew him on the spot. Then he forged a good two edged sword and shining armour for himself, and having saddled the best horse of Mimer's stable, he left the smithy to look for new adventures.

For a long time he travelled aimlessly about, saw mountains and valleys, rivers

and lakes, cities and hamlets, until he
at last arrived at the seashore. He em-
barked with his good horse, and was cast
by a gale on the rocky coast of an unknown country. The noble animal climbed
courageously up the stony beach, and carried its rider to an enchanted castle which
was surrounded by a wall of flames. For
a moment Siegfried stood irresolute. Suddenly the voice of the little bird sounded
again above him, "Break the charm.
Straight into the flames with a bold dash.
A most lovely maiden will be thy reward."

The youth took courage, spurred his
steed, and with a plunge horse and rider
disappeared in the flames, which were at
once extinguished. The charm was broken.
Before him lay a wonderful castle. Siegfried penetrated into its interior, and
was amazed to find every living creature in a profound sleep within; the horses
in their stalls, the grooms in the stab-
les, the cook at the hearth. When he
entered the high hall a lovely scene presented itself to his view. On a couch the

most exquisite form of a woman lay sleeping. Her golden hair was strewn with precious stones, and her limbs were clothed in the most costly garments.

The young hero looked for a while, lost in admiration. Then bending down to her, he pressed a passionate kiss on her rosy lips. Brunhilde, the fair sleeper, opened her eyes, and at the same time every living being in the castle awoke.

At the prospect of new adventures Siegfried could not be kept back a long time by Brunhilde. They parted with the solemn promise of meeting again.

The legend of Siegfried's youthful exploits and his home-coming is full of romance and happiness. But if we listen to the continuation of his story we shall find how every human feeling has its place in the hero's biography, great joy, deep sorrow, passionate love, glowing hatred, heroism and perfidy, cowardice and high courage, until at last the legend of Siegfried ends in a pitiful wail of grief.

List of illustrations

There also exists a <u>large</u> edition of the

Legends of the Rhine

by **Wilhelm Ruland**

with many illustrations from paintings by
celebrated artists

beautifully bound ℳ 4,50.

———

The present small edition offers a choice
of the most beautiful Rhine legends from
<u>Worms to Cologne</u>. On the other hand the
<u>large</u> edition comprises the <u>whole basin</u> of
the river from its rise on the Gothard in
Switzerland until it throws itself into the
North-Sea (the side-valleys included). The
book can be highly recommended to all those,
who want to get a deeper knowledge of the
peculiar poetic charm of the noble river, all
the more, as the author has taken great care
in considering the historical background of
the legends.